M

D1287421

NEW  DIRECTIONS 29

# N D

# New Directions in Prose and Poetry  29

**Edited by J. Laughlin**

with Peter Glassgold and Frederick R. Martin

**A New Directions Book**

ACKNOWLEDGMENTS

Grateful acknowledgment is made to the editors and publishers of books
and magazines where some of the selections in this volume first appeared:
for Martin Bax, *Ambit* (London); for Warren Jay Hecht, *Anon 1973*
(Copyright © 1973 by Warren Jay Hecht), *The Lake Superior Review*
(Copyright © 1972 by The Lake Superior Review), *The Michigan Daily
Magazine,* and *Shoplifters Will Be Persecuted* (Copyright © 1972 by
David G. Dumo); for Denise Levertov, *American Report* (Copyright
© 1973 by Denise Levertov Goodman); for Artur Lundkvist, *London
Magazine, Stand* (England), and *Transatlantic Review;* for James Purdy,
*Antaeus* (Copyright © 1974 by James Purdy); for Piero Sanavio, *The
Texas Quarterly* (Copyright © 1966 by The University of Texas).


Manufactured in the United States of America
First published clothbound (ISBN: 0–8112–0539–8) and as
New Directions Paperbook 378 (ISBN: 0–8112–0540–1) in 1974
Published simultaneously in Canada by McClelland & Stewart, Ltd.


New Directions Books are published for James Laughlin
by New Directions Publishing Corporation,
333 Sixth Avenue, New York 10014

75-18291

# CONTENTS

*Walter Abish*

How the Comb Gives a Fresh Meaning to the Hair        62

*David Antin*

is this the right place?        23

*Homero Aridjis*

Six Poems from *Los Espacios Azules*        95

*Martin Bax*

The Crucifixion Disease        2

*Cid Corman*

Eleven Poems        110

*Coleman Dowell*

First Person Biography        142

*Lawrence Ferlinghetti*

Pablo        1

*Warren Jay Hecht*

from *Fiction as Life Style*        172

*Yumiko Kurahashi*

The Boy Who Became an Eagle        116

*Denise Levertov*

Four Poems        57

*Artur Lundkvist*

Eight Poems        164

*Marichiko*
 Five poems  54

*Michael McClure*
 Four Poems  161

*Toby Olson*
 Corridors  82

*Thomas Parkinson*
 Pablo Neruda  182

*A. Poulin, Jr.*
 Six Poems from *Imaginary Beings of the Will*  134

*James Purdy*
 Lily's Party  99

*Piero Sanavio*
 Antilla  13

*Tennessee Williams*
 Two Poems  77

*Al Young*
 New Orleans Intermission  138

Notes on Contributors  184

# PABLO

Pablo no invoco tu nombre en vano
   Tu muerte la muerte Chilena
Pablo Araucano del viento pampero
Pablo Pablo escapado en los Andes cuarenta-y-nueve
Pablo con tu Chile Libre a París cuarenta-y-nueve
     con tus ojos de Picasso
      con tu política de Picasso
       con tu cabeza de tortuga
Pablo conmigo con Cuba Libre sesenta-y-uno
Pablo Pablo con tu Isla Negra
     con tu Mathilda
      con tus proas de barco
Pablo Pablo escapado esta vez
      atrás la puerta escondida
     de la muerte
   con tu 'Residencia en la Tierra'
    ahora en la Tierra para siempre
  con tu libertad ahora en la Tierra
Pablo Pablo con tu voz de libertad Chilena
   que no invoco que no invoco ahora
      en vano
   en tu muerte
       la muerte Chilena!

—lawrence ferlinghetti

First read at a Neruda Memorial in San Francisco
Oct. '73, shortly after the Chilean militarist
insurrection which overthrew Allende's Socialist
government. Pablo Neruda died just then in Chile.

# THE CRUCIFIXION DISEASE

Excerpts from the novel *The Hospital Ship*

MARTIN BAX

## The Gibraltar Sequence

Very cautiously the big atomic-powered hospital ship was creeping up towards Europe. They had swung back from the Pacific for no very good reason, really, and cruised slowly up the coast of Africa. They had kept well clear of South Africa itself and not even seen a sight of the famous Table Mountain. From Angola they had picked up a group of dying and sick children who appeared to have been in a Catholic orphanage, but no adults were available to tell them how the children had been deserted. They had been standing or lying on a quayside as a picket boat came in from the hospital ship lying further out. They were dressed in rags, looked half starved and did not know how they came to be where they were. They each clasped a tightly rolled scroll in their hands and were reluctant to release them. The doctors gently prized them from their hands. Each child held a Catholic baptismal certificate, but none of the children answered to the name that appeared engraved on the particular parchment they held. They shook their heads when called by the listed names and shouted aloud strange unchristian names like Xuna.

Further up the coast they had again sent a party ashore and found a small African town functioning quite normally. They had been able to purchase fresh fruits and even to replenish the ship's vast storeroom with some tinned foods that the locals were happy to sell them. But there was no news. Tafteria reported all wave lengths dead. They had hoped that from South Africa some stations would still be broadcasting, and the constant radio search had been intensified. There was only one which was on the air. It was broadcasting over and over again obscenities and swearwords in Afrikaans. The sequences were never repeated exactly in the same order, and there were occasionally moments when short abusive speeches were addressed to Kaffirs. The listeners decided that the messages were being generated by a computer. Did the programmers hope to attract some reply? The *Hopeful* did not know what reply to make so they transmitted their call signal only, but there was no additional response.

Now, as they came on past the equator and ever closer to Europe, the air became alive again. Atonal music, bunches of static, half sentences about budgerigar care, cake recipes, origami instructions for making parts of the human body in paper (like heart and kidneys). Tafteria, their mad Welsh wireless chief, was busy again. "News" she would shout and rush out of the wireless with her rolls of paper full of bizarre messages. Finally one message dominated all the rest. "They are using us," it said; it came in from all over— Dubrovnik, Montreuil, Danzig, Oulu, Narvik and finally Gibraltar, which lay ahead of them. "What for?" they cabled back, but no reply was vouchsafed.

The Rock then as evening was coming on. Very slowly they slid in, ready to turn and flee if they were attacked. They had swung in in a big arc from the Atlantic so they had approached from the northwest. The Captain wanted to have a good look at the airport. All eyes were on the runway which stretches out into the sea. Would a plane speed out to investigate them? But no, the runway was not in use, a great plane lay crumpled and crashed on it.

Beyond the runway lay Waterport Wharf and the North Mole. There was some sort of construction work, it looked like, going on along the quays. There were what appeared to be huge arrays of rather small derricks mounted all along the quays. They were short, say sixteen feet high, had an upright piece about two feet stretching up above the side arms stretching out either side for about four feet. Curious shape. Cruciform when you stared at them and thought about them. Crosses. They were crosses.

"Something to welcome us," said Sir Max. "To remind us of what we've always been proudest of in our own civilization." Glasses were raised and trained on them now. Men, dead men, were attached to them. The ship dropped anchor outside, not far away from the end of the runway; the Captain was not going into that harbour. There were men attached, nailed to all the crosses along all the quays. They blew a long blast on their hooter and waited. A host of birds flew up from the crosses. Crows will pluck out the eyes of living sheep. What will the scavenger gull do to the dead human being? No one human moved on the shore.

They lowered some of their motorboats, and volunteer groups set off to examine the crosses. Some of the men might still be alive. On board the ship crew and staff crowded the rail, watched in silence as the boats plied in and tied up at Waterport Wharf—just where the Tangier boats had been used to sail. Row upon row of men looked blindly down at the shore party. Some of the younger doctors felt they should listen to the hearts of the victims to check they were dead, but they had no ladders and they couldn't reach up the ten to twelve feet to their chests. The older staff merely pointed to livid changes in the feet, the dried blood round the nails in their feet.

By now it was quite dark, and a small party decided to go and look for other humans. They followed the road up into the town. At first all seemed deserted, but as they came to Main Street a little old lady came scuttling down Crutchett's Ramp. They didn't mean to grab her, but she nevertheless shrank against the wall from them in terror, screaming, "I was only going out to try to get a little tea." They hastened to reassure her and tried to explain who they were, but fear overcame her, and she hurried back the way she had come, still clutching the empty envelope she had intended to fill with tea.

But they became aware that there were inhabitants about. The hotels were empty, the banks and offices were shut, but some of the little shops along Main Street showed a little cautious light—candlelight. Some of the inhabitants were there, shut into their houses, doing nothing, not coming out to welcome them but present and alive. Presently they began to knock on doors, summon people out and try to find out what had happened. There was an unwillingness to talk, a withdrawal, a sliding away even when a well-known neighbour appeared as well. The details of what had happened had to be wrung out with direct question after direct question.

"Who were they?" "Did they kill all the men?" "Why did they do it?" "Where did they come from?" "Where have they gone?" To all they had less than clear answers. They were men in grey suits—respectable men, they were. Some of them had their wives and families with them. Gibraltar being a nice place they said they'd brought the families along for a bit of a holiday. Nice people they were really when you got to know them.

"Why did they do it" Hard to say. They said they had to. It was their job, and they'd been told to. They just left one man alive—old Harry—he's wooden legs, and they said they didn't fancy hammering through that wood. Any rate he's nearly dead. "All men are dogs," he (Harry) says.

They did it very quickly, very efficiently, you know. They had guns and so on if they needed them, but there wasn't any shooting. Three sons I had, God bless them. I don't know where they've gone. Drove off in their cars and vans as soon as the job was done. They said they had a lot of work to do and didn't see themselves getting a proper holiday all year. Poor souls. On their way to North Africa they were. Or had they come from there?

If there was a pause in the questioning, "Is that all then, because if you don't mind I'll be shutting up and going to bed now. Good night then, good night."

The ship had nothing really to offer. There are no medicines for the dead. But they decided that in the morning they could at least remove the crosses and arrange burial for the dead. The psychiatrists said the inhabitants were in a state of shock, and if the crosses and bodies were removed some more normal form of mourning might develop. They felt the ship should stay under the Rock and help the inhabitants work their way through the mourning process.

Around three in the morning lights and fires on the shore awoke the ship. Everybody tumbled out onto the deck to stare at the shore. Someone soon after dusk must have driven round and sprayed each cross and corpse with petrol. The night watch had suddenly seen a glimmer of light near the bottom of the North Mole, and then with a great flash of sounds flames had swept round, and every cross was suddenly burning brightly. Many of them had been tilted crazily forward so that the bodies hung over the sea and, as the flames took hold, there was added to their row the noise and the hiss and splash of burning flesh and wood falling into the water.

Soon drifting across the water to the ship came the smoke. Smell first of petrol then of roasting meat. People turned away, covering their faces, and fled down to their air-conditioned rooms. None of the medical staff argued when the Captain took a policy decision without consulting them. He abandoned Gibraltar. He pulled his anchors and sailed at once. The fires sank below the horizon, the stench was blown off the ship as it pulsed on through the night into the Mediterranean basin.

In the morning they were clear of all land but steaming east fast. Bob and Euan breakfasted together and then went up on deck before going down for their daily ward work.

"Tafteria had it wrong again," said Bob.

"What do you mean?" Euan asked.

"Those messages she kept getting, you know, 'they are using us.' That's not what they were saying. What they were saying was, 'They're crucifying us.' She can't put that down to static. It was her deaf Welsh ears."

"Yes," said Sir Maximov, who was up on the deck breathing deeply the fresh morning air, "they were telling us about a disease process, and we didn't recognize it. We ought to have done, it's been well known for years."

"What disease?" said Euan.

"The crucifixion disease," said Sir Max, "it can start in early infancy."


*The Psychopathology of Everyman**

Human infants are provided with powerful innate release mechanisms through which they command adults to attend to their vital needs. Since human infancy is so protracted and so dangerous, these commands elicit biological responses in adults of a most powerful kind. Cataclysmic breakdown of this interaction is at the core of child abuse. "His crying," said a mother of a battered baby, "his crying seemed to follow me round the house, I could not stop it—and I could not escape."

The breakdown, the paroxysms of violence, is always followed by denial and confabulation, epitomized by, "It did not seem to be me that did it."

This denial and the fantastic explanations offered for the injury meet, nearly always, with collusion by the spouse. This compulsive

---

* A paper by Christopher Ounsted, a friend of the author's, presented at a medical meeting.—Editor

denial of the obvious is shared, with relief, by doctors and social workers. "I cannot bear," said one such, "I cannot bear to believe that anyone could do such a thing."

The Psalmist knew this behaviour. "Blessed shall he be that taketh thy children; and throweth them against stones."

So why were we, in the modern West, so long delayed in our acceptance of the syndrome?

I think it was no historic accident that recognition came after Hitler's war. We had been forced to see, unwillingly, that a whole nation of ancient Christian civility could suddenly degenerate into a frenzy of barbaric cruelty. This led many to admit that there lay buried in the common humanity of all modern men a violent beast awaiting release. Be that as it may, denial is a universal feature of the syndrome. Denial leads to recurrence. The paroxysm of violence generates its own return.

Either side, or both, may have defects which set the scene for the explosion. Henry Kempe has taught us, and our own experiences echo his at every point, that a common pattern of parental rearing can be discerned. The parents were themselves unloved children, children to whom nothing was given, but much was demanded. In some cases they had themselves been battered. They now expect from their own infant that he should, from birth, love them unreservedly—he must in particular never excite in them that disquiet which drives adults to respond to infantile crying.

When repeatedly abused children are watched they show a diagnostic behaviour pattern. I have called it "frozen watchfulness." They make no sounds. They keep quite still. They look you in the eyes, but they give out no facial signals. They have learned not to ask, by cry or word; not to demand, by approach or flight; not to influence, by smile or frown.

Frozen watchfulness, that end product of repeated abuse, declares an adaptation to a world where a loving and loved adult unpredictably and without warning is transformed into a brutal aggressor—and then immediately reverts to good mothering once more.

Both parents came from families where violence ruled and had done for generations. Fear and anger bound the two together. Their other children were dirty and unmanageable. Their house, their persons and their biographies would excite disgust in all of us.

But that was four years ago. Now the whole family is a stable and loving unity. Cleanliness and kindness and a sort of simple courtesy are what strikes one in them all. The change began when they, at a crisis, learned that what they did had not cut them off from the rest of humanity.

The psychopathology of the Battered Baby Syndrome is basically quite simple. It is part of human nature itself. It is the psychopathology of Everyman. If *we* can grasp this then, like the parents of the blind baby, perhaps there will be hope for us too.

The Roman poet Catullus knew that this dilemma was universal. I will English what he wrote: "I love-and-hate, and if you ask why? —I don't know. But that's how it is, and it crucifies me."

### World Affairs: The Piraeus Piece

The *Hopeful* had planned to go up into the Gulf of Lyons and visit some of the towns in the south of France. But Marseilles had been one of the towns that cabled and no one really fancied another crucifixion scene. They had heard nothing, however, from Greece or Turkey so the ship now plunged on towards Athens. Hoping that there some shore contact would enable them to determine what was happening and to define more precisely what the ship's own role should be in their daily dealing with what the psychiatrists were calling "the crucifixion disease." The patients suffered, they said, from an obsessional neurosis—an unavoidable urge to crucify people.

The ship's move, however, was an ill conceived one because it led to almost direct confrontation with the crucifixion men. Piraeus has many quaysides and harbours twisting and tumbling along the Attic coastline. They anchored again offshore among the fishing boats, not far from the quayside where the boats for Aegina and the islands left. It was before dawn, and light was just beginning to come up, but on shore they could see lights and flares; hammering and screams became audible as soon as the anchors were down and the engines stilled. Again the large shore boat was lowered, and the anxious decision taken to send in an exploratory party. Their boat crept in as the light grew. The flare torches dimmed as the light grew stronger, but when the boat was still fifty yards out, they were hailed in a cultured mid-Atlantic voice: "No closer or we fire." And to emphasize, the clatter of a gun and bullets whistling among the vedette's masts. They sheered off back to the hospital ship and lay offshore and watched as the sun came up and the trees of crosses sprouted on the shore.

They realized they had arrived as the job was being finished; the crosses were mainly up. They could see beyond a line of grey cars with one or two armoured vehicles beside with men on top with machine guns. Beyond that some sort of barrier had been erected across the street and pinned back a crowd of women, some older men, and children who stood silenced by the menace of the guns mounted on the cars. What should the doctors do in their ship, could they intervene or should they just watch? It was a role they knew well—one of sustained hopelessness. Watching the young girl with leukaemia, the attractive dark-haired lass with the breast cancer, the upright fifty-five-year-old with his lung hacking his life out. Negative capability, a doctor called it, being aware and doing nothing. Keeping some sort of hopeful face towards the future. The *Hopeful* loaded its boats with emergency teams, blood, cardiac resuscitation units, all the paraphernalia, and waited.

Now the men in grey had completed their task and silently withdrew to their cars. They set off rattling away south down the road to Glyffada Beach and along that rocky shore to Sunion. No doubt to offer some sort of oblation at the famous temple on that rocky promontory.

As soon as they moved all the ship's boats tore in towards the shore. Long before they got there came the wail from the crowds as they crushed down the barriers and rushed forward to the crosses. As the doctors, nurses and orderlies climbed ashore with their little battery-run resuscitatory trolleys, women rushed at them, wailing and weeping. Their arms were almost torn out as they were pulled or pushed towards this or that cross.

Although Euan spoke no Greek he could understand well enough, he found. The women with their weathered faces, their long black dresses, their headscarves, tears pouring down their faces, crying: "I have lost my son." They crowded round the *Hopeful's* staff, pressing up against them and preventing them from getting to work. What should you do when you did get to a cross? Pull the cross down first? Which was difficult—deep holes had been cut for the bases and still soft concrete had been pushed in round them. Or climb up and wrench out the nails and lower the man down—and then what? What was the modern treatment for crucifixion?

In the 50s a German professor of anatomy crucified some of his medical students. He didn't use nails but bandaged them to their crosses. They lost consciousness very quickly—that not being a good position for breathing in—and the respiratory distress led quickly to cardiac embarrassment. Here in this old seaport many of the men were already dead. Dying of shock, perhaps, in the initial moments, but others could be resuscitated. They were far too many to take on board the ship, so treatment was given them then and there on the quay. Packets of O blood were rushed ashore and, lying the patient on the quayside, with relatives acting as willing drip stands to hold the transfusion bottle, blood was poured into them. The stigmata were sutured. Antibiotic cover and passive tetanus immunisation were pumped in. Hearts shocked back into action. These were not the only cases the doctors had to treat. Women had been savagely assaulted, children struck by falling masonry. As soon as it was known that doctors were on shore people crowded round them with sick and dying relatives. All sorts of diseases seemed rampant. Euan suddenly realized he was examining his first case of leprosy. That whole old seaport became one massive hospital.

What impressed itself on Euan during the long day was the noise. The continual shout, jabber and almost hysterical scream of people involved in a disaster. The clangour was incessant, and it formed a background to the quietly spoken words which he exchanged with his nurse and with his orderly. "Have we some catgut? I think I ought to put a couple of sutures through this muscle belly. Yes, give him a shot of morphia. Scissors please." And occasionally: "Please, please, please stop screaming." Towards sunset long blasts of recall were blown by the *Hopeful* sirens. Euan sent his orderly and nurse off but was still there himself it seemed hours later.

A woman had carried a four-year-old child up to him and pulled back a shawl to show him swollen glands in the axillae and groin. Euan began to palpate them, even in his fatigue curious to know what the cause of the swelling was. But then he glanced at the child's pasty face and realized there were no respiratory movements of the chest wall. He took his stethoscope and held it for the statutory minute over the precordium listening for the faintest evidence of heart beats. There were none, the child was dead. He looked up at the mother and said, shaking his head:

"He's dead, dead, dead." And shook his head hard at her. But the woman thrust the child at him shouting the two words of spoken English, she'd learnt:

"Doctor, doctor, medzines, medzines."

He seemed to be pressed back against a wall himself, and he was unable to escape, and he had to reach out with his hands and push the woman with her burden away from him. He managed to turn her round so that now she was back against the wall, but in some way she managed both to hold the child and cling to his sleeve. He looked round at the many bystanders for help, but they looked on with uncomprehending eyes. He turned back again to the woman, shaking his head again and wishing he could remember the Greek word for death.

Suddenly someone pushed firmly through the crowd, reached forward and took his wrists from behind in a firm grasp and pulled him round to face her. It was Sheila. Euan felt embarrassed to face her because he realized that he too had been—was—crying, and the tears rolled down his cheeks. Sheila wiped his eyes with her hands, bent forward and kissed his lips. She said:

"Come on, Euan, we're leaving. The ship's packed with patients, there is no more we can do on shore, we must give up and go where we can work." He allowed himself to be led away.

"The dead," said Sheila, "are not our patients."

The woman with the dead child made a feeble attempt to follow them. He heard her stumble a few paces after them, a final cry of "Doctor, medzines," and then the excited sweating crowd separated them finally.

The hospital ship turned back south from Athens and began wending her way down through the islands, uncertain whether to attempt another landfall within the Mediterranean basin. At dusk a group of medical staff had come out from their wards and operating suites and were standing, not speaking, apart to allow the wind to catch and cool and freshen them. Some noise, movement suddenly caught their attention, and they all turned. There outside her wireless station, standing, crying silently, was Tafteria. In each hand she held sheaves of opened cables, and as they turned towards her she thrust her arms and shook the cables like leaves, demanding with her action that they should pluck them from her hands.

No one however moved towards her at once. They looked at Tafteria. She was not tall but was hugely proportioned. Great shoulders, huge bosom, thick waist. Her hair, which was white, she kept rather short. She wore rather thick-lensed pale-rimmed glasses, and it was difficult to decide whether her rather too orderly teeth were all artificial or not. Normally her warm but spinsterish personality led people to tease her about the deficiencies of her peculiar communications section. Now no one said anything, awed by the tears that streamed down her face. After a moment they simply came forward and took a cable each and moved away to read them.

They all bore the same message. Indeed they had guessed the message. "They are crucifying us." They passed them round, and the assortment of addresses rang in their heads: Beirut, Budapest, Ostia, Smyrna, Port Mahon, Bizerta. All the same message—"They are crucifying us." Euan was reminded of George MacBeth's attempt years before to describe this event with his sinister poem game, "Fin du globe." There complex and meaningless postcards had been presented from all over the world.

"Too complex," thought Euan now, "too complex." Ends can always be put simply.

Tafteria, her hands empty, still stood there crying hopelessly. Sir Maximov moved over to her, placed his hands on her shoulders and shook her slightly.

"Go back inside there, Tafteria," he said, "and send a message to God: 'Why hast thou forsaken us?' Got it? 'Why hast thou forsaken us.'" Tafteria looked at him, nodded and went to do his bidding.

Later in the evening they were strolling the decks when suddenly Tafteria was before them again. This time she was her usual sharp self.

"Your prepaid reply, Sir Maximov," she said, thrusting the cable at him and retreating into the wireless station at once.

"Quick work," said Sir Maximov, taking the cable and slitting it open, "must have been a hot line." He read it and passed it over to Euan. It read as follows:

JESUS CHRIST ALIVE STOP WONDERFULLY WELL STOP
WONDERFULLY HAPPY STOP IN PARADISE STOP ENDS

The message was unsigned. Sir Maximov took the paper back and tore it into small pieces and let them go slowly over the side.

"Been there a fair time too by all accounts. Wouldn't mind it myself. Not bad really for just nine hours on the gallows."

# ANTILLA

PIERO SANAVIO

*for Ramon Enrique Bauzá*

*"Llaman los indios Boriquen á la isla que agora los chripstianos llaman
Sanot Iohan, la qual está al Oriente desta Isla Española, veynte é cinco ó
treynta leguas. Y en la mitad de este camino está la isla de la Mona en diez
é siete grados de la linia equinoçial."* Natural y general historia de las
Indias, islas y Tierra-Firme del Mar Oçeano
—Gonzalo Fernando de Oviedo

### I

Four hundred years, the Bull
kneeling for resurrection
to hornéd moons and seas.
". . . better a pirate than a Christian
king, death (better)
than trembling lips."

that's Chris
Columbus:

           The tired Wop
sipping his fill of poisonous daydreams
to Diego and past him.
       "A thick Sargasso sea
boils sails under my bald skull
in the dry season of this Valladolid:
haunts memories of sun-gold, moon-gold,
wags its tongue crabbed with meridians,
ebbs full of wonderful fish
            and voices
—winds, birds, trees.
In my last trip into the bowels of the Deep,
I saw twin moons over marshland,
dreaming of the Bull."

## II

the conquest &
first exploitation
of the island:

                        Juan Ponce
swaps Indians for tin,
young Salcedo skindives for chief Broyóan
                    in the mud of Guarabo.
"In the Holy Name of Our Lord,
Savior and Castilian,
                        I possess
this island and one third of its
gold, if there's any:
                        two thirds
to the Bastard of Spain
for landlubbering profiteers
sitting fat behind scales.
Guadalupe, name of my shame.

the XVIth cent.
epidemic that
killed most of the
Indians:

Pox and vermin crawling into the sex
of my tawny slaves: the disease
fingers my marrow, cracks its way
into my bones. My armor squeaks
rust.
            Jesus of Spain:
on Your divine instrument and his
gold (and this land)
lay Your protecting hand."

Poor Ponce lost his job, died,
                all his money was robbed
by the Mayor of Havana.

Drake's last year:

Betsy's boy turned up to kill,
                painted his face,
a cannonball broke his plate,
                set sail to Trujillo.

Dutchman
Henrique:

Hendricksz couldn't take the heat,
burnt the library of Balbuena.

The soil was good for sugar:
best crops came with black labor.

III

Had them shipped over
from Guinea and Angola,
                their backwardness
an insurance policy against rebellion.
Cardinal Cisneros
                granted the license of import
to the Padres Jerónimos,
                Carlos of Austria
okayed the deal but
                vetoed the sale of Arabs:
"a dangerous race, wily, jealous
                of its liberty,
a potential threat to our peace."

At sundown
        pelicans plummet into the purple
                sea,
their gunmetal blackness soon emerging,
                then down,
        shoots upwards and then
                down,
for today's last sardine. Steelband
throbbings from Hilton's Kaaba
                in fashionable Condado.
On these waters flatbottomed skiffs
glided 'tween reef and reed,
adelantándose sigilosamente in asshole
                        darkness, on
the 18th day of October, 1529.
The Caribs sprang to attack at midnight,
burned ships,
                killed
                blacks and whites,
withdrew at sunup to the Isleta—

After Hendricksz, for two hundred years,
poverty
and desolation
and isolation.

The sea turned into dust,
the thin leaves of madness
grew
on the roofs of palaces and huts.

Only maggots were fat.

IV

Merchants flocked in from Spain,
got rich,

the sugar crisis of
the 1880's:

trapiches were left to weeds
in midday's glare:
                Negroni saw his sister's belly
naked for his hands,
a shaded waterpool to thirst
or impotence.
                "Brother, brother,
                hold me tight,
                force me
                and . . ."
Preferred to dream of subjective landscapes
or hide from that body
                in other bodies
and suddenly life left him, a bleat-
ing ghost in a barrel of vinegar.
She got married in Spain
                (". . . force me . . ."),
he turned his eyes to the . . .
evoking her for . . .
Last fragments of flesh, torn between sheets:
                Gloria
or whatwasit.
                ("I never dared to meet . . .")

As they were scared to meet
                to free themselves
of that bondage, called Spain,
to meet and free . . .
As they were unable to yank themselves
free of themselves to be
                what

they were meant to be
or whatwasit . . .

V

Rafael Cordero,
a XIXth cent.
school teacher &
son of slaves:

"Hubo en Borinquen un hombre" when old
Rafa, "con la dádiva en la mano,"
taught Baldorioty and Tapia:
                    meaning
to bleach his skin to fashion or
haunted by the beats at the Wall,
when his forefathers hugged the night,
talked to the ghost and the toad,
called Quimbamba, in their dreams?
                    or Nowhere and that was
                    Africa: never seen by young
                    Rafa.
                         Till, one day, wrinkled father
                    Cordero
                         (the sores
                    from the chain still on his
                    ankles) said, or shouted,
"That's our Mother, beyond this
sea!" and danced a wild jig,
                    and young Rafa, yolk-
                    eyed and smiling, sang after
                    him, not knowing
                    and other blacks answered
                    from the fields,
¡bomba!
                    Men of the Antilla
calling home, over the setting
sun.

                    White folks, in white
guayaberas and Panama hats, sip
Cuba libre or tea:
                    "The peseta goes
down, down. Better
                    switch to the buck."

. . . likely, he didn't mean it:
and he taught them because he believed
it was a job he could do,
no matter what his father had been.

A for Anger, B for Beast, C for
Carrion, D for Degeneration or
Destruction. Till it came. A faint

the Lares Outcry,
1868:

whisper, though they called it
"Grito": from the farms on the
hills, and it was white, like
the speeches, the papers, the
bombs.

In the strongbox
paid by the City,
where your body rotted
with a view of the sea,
you did not think
or hope,
just waited:
for a man dressed in black,
black his skin and his
thoughts,
to change the geography
you had taught: and that history.
(Died in 1868,
five years
before abolition).

VI

the pirate Cofresí,
killed in 1825,
& then
don Pedro
Albizu
Campos:

The young pirate, before him:
caught in Guayama,
aged about 26,
and flogged before being shot.
"Stole from the rich,
gave to the poor."

Crossing the Yard, from the Widener steps,
toward phony Byzantine Memorial Hall,

he did not know his color, yet.
Ponce split him from Ramos,

the indepen-
dentista upheaval
of Oct. 1950:

Jayuya saw the guns and the bombs.
Old San Juan watched, as his haggard
frame was carried by
                    circus attendants
through the smoke of tearbombs.
Albizu: the heart whiter than . . .

                    Proud like Jesus,
                    the same sin undid him.
                    Nigger,
                    but the trenches knew no
                    discrimination.
                    Proud like Farinata,
                    the same hunger undid him:
                    mounted the firewheel.
                    As humorless as a cornerstone.
Victory smiled to Sancho: a paper
bull, with Mambrin's hat and
spear. You
                    —an enemy to the people.


VII

                    Garbage can of the Carib sea,

but that was before the Pretorians
came from Washington with gifts.
The new king,
                    a scarecrow with money-
bills, taumaturgical, and the touch
against v.d.,
                    built hostels for the rich,
sold T.V.'s on installment to the poor.
                    ". . . better a pirate . . ."
High percent of incest,
                    rape, dopeaddiction.

Operation
Bootstrap:

"Let's destroy their dependence on the soil
                    (they said),

their traditional family structure,
hence
their culture, or what's left.
Let's,
for instance, sell them canned tomatoes
at a lower price than the tomatoes they
produce. Once we've gained their
trust, if we create enough
job opportunities
in a nearby area, we'll be able to
condition them to
factory work.
Then we'll go bankrupt.
Jobless, and now
without any confidence in their
past, they'll be easily convinced of
the advantages of emigration.
Maximum wages?
fifty cents per hour.
The island
will be in our hands. You can
set up factories, there, enjoy
tax deductions and no competition."


VIII

the Bull, a
religious & astral
symbol of
Puerto Rico,
according to a
XVIIth cent.
Dominican:

The tail curls up in Cabo Roxo, his hindlegs
tucked in beneath it.
A forepaw in Culebra,
splintered. From Cangrejos to Las Croabas
the horns, long past the beach.
On the hills
of his spine, monkeys from Andalusia swung
happy from the trees, wilder than
niggers:
1800 or thereabout,
black Frenchmen killing white,
in Hispaniola.

Under the flamboyanes, next to the Wall,
in the big-framed wooden house, musty with

sweat and perfumes, a Maria blushes pretty
at the honest proposals of her beau,
her virginal thighs moist under stiff slips.
She lets him kiss her hand, and
sees him off to the funereal landeau.
Her father gags upstairs, pants
blind drunk, mounting the nurse.
                    Mother
kneels, holds her beads, weeps,
tells her sins: the confessor makes a cross
of absolution, over his stinking breath
from too much food and bad teeth.

Paternal rule: it was.
                    Left a prison
called Princesa, in homage to a never-to-be
Queen,

from Spanish to
Northamerican
rule:
                    left churches, mulattoes, t.b.
Then Teddy, on horseback, cursing the saddle
against his aging pelvis, called it
Carib Switzerland,
                    chewed his carrot
on it, like a rabbit, showed the stick.


IX

"Let's start a revolution, then a counter
            revolution: there's money, in it."
"Not here. Not this year. We lost too much with
            that Cuban invasion."
"We made up for the loss with what we earned
            in Santo Domingo."

the
Alliance
for Progress:
"Well . . . unrest is bad for our economy, let's
            rather get into the Alianza."
Moscoso came up, smiling from the top of his
            father's drugstores, toothpaste and anti-
            conceptionals made in P.R.
            to be sold in South America.

They had sent a few boys to Santo Domingo;
they sent a few more to Vietnam,

a few more
to learn how to take hard drugs
and shoot from the hip
and need more drugs
and kill some Charlies
and go back home
                    shaking with fear
and hallucinations
                    for Old Glory.


The shadow of El Morro grows
like a spider on the small
bay: voices
            from the clubs
talking of Virginny and the Eighties
(1800)
when it was so easy
to make a fast buck.
            (Nostalgia's as thick as
            molasses, in the club:
            moths and wild bats
            knock their wings
            against the panes).
". . . drugs, that's the answer:
call Chicago, call Palermo, call . . ."
"No need: we grow everything here."


San Juan '73. The black waiter, blacker
than my shoes, says,
                    "My parents came from
Spain."
                    Bull,
geographic freak, dream, or
                    otro embuste tropical,
you surely sleep a long rest, under
                    those hills.
Perhaps the slumber of a foetus, or
                    (perhaps)
the final trance of the dead.

(1963–1973)

# is this the right place?

david antin


      when i was asked what i wanted to talk
  about       before i came here      i picked up
the telephone    in san diego and     bill
  miller from the philadelphia art museum
spoke to me on the phone     said "what are
  you going to talk about?"      and     i had
about     five seconds     to decide     and
  in the five seconds    i realized      that
theres something peculiar about talking on a
  telephone     when youre three thousand five
  hundred miles away    which is approximate-
ly the distance     long winded crows
  take when they go directly from san diego
    to philadelphia     and i remembered
philadelphia very vaguely     as i kept trying to think of philadelphia     im an old
  new yorker    as youll probably recognize
from my accent    which is fairly marked
    and i thought of philadelphia "what does
  philadelphia have?"     well it has all sorts
of things     i remembered the rodin museum
    the franklin institute     a ninety mile

drive which seemed to take hours        that i
  couldnt put together with ninety mile drives
in california        because in california
      when you drive ninety miles        you make
  it in about an hour and a half or less
      and when you drive from new york to phi-
  ladelphia you dont make it in an hour and
a half        so that the space was different
      and there was the friendly voice on the
  other side of the telephone and i said "well
      ill talk about 'is this the right place?'"
      because i had a feeling        that it
might be the right place and        it might not
  be the right place        but the rightness of
place is something you learn        progress-
      ively        apparently        not something you
know instantly        when i came here        in the
  plane        this time        and ive come back
and forth so many times now im beginning to
  suffer from air shock between flights
      when i got on the plane        i had the
feeling        i started out early in the day
      it was about 12 oclock        to be on a
  plane        12 oclock on a plane is in some
  ways the worst possible time to get on a
plane because        what happens is        you start
  out in the daylight and you wind up in the
      night        and there never was any day        and
  its odd        you feel that youre travelling
into the past        though technically youve gone
  into the future and lost the present        but
you cant really come to terms with that
      somehow youve lost the day and youve gone
  into some time thats anterior        to your
  time        and you dont know what to make of it
      youve been enveloped by night        you look
out of the window        you know        youre sitting on a plane        and you start investing
  in anything possible that happens on planes
      earphones drinks whatever        and you
  plug in everything        because you may as
well do the plane experience        otherwise why

do it at all?      and you pay your two dollars for earphones your dollar fifty for a
   bloody mary      although its earlier in the
day than you would ever drink in your life and
      you turn on the sound system and there
   is this odd sound coming out      quickly you
turn      you want to know whether you should
      turn on corporate art      theres a lecture
thats going on about "art as business"
      and i thought that was terrific      but
   i couldnt get it      because someone was
talking about mergers      theres a ninety minute cycle      the problem of time keeps
coming up      and someone is talking about
mergers      mergers of conglomerates      and
   at that moment i wasnt interested in mergers
   because i didnt have a conglomerate i wanted
to merge      i wanted to hear about art as
   business but art as business was forty-five
minutes away and i wasnt going to make it so
      i turned on music and      i tried for the
music i thought would be interesting      and
   i hoped i was going to get brahms third sym-
phony and i came up in the middle of schelomo
      and it went on and it was interesting
      because it was very muddy      you know
the earphones are      i suppose theyre as good
   earphones as they could get on an airplane
      and what you get is a sound that you
vaguely recognize      the element of recognition in this is more than anything else because no pitch is very distinct      so chords
for example      have one note you hear and two
   you guess      which is a rather impressive
conceptual art form      and for a while you
   listen      and then they put on a movie
      and you dont really want to hear the mo-
vie      because there is a movie about a ro-
deo clown      you know this because you see
   his face and its all white and somebody is
beating him up and      you dont know why and
   you dont really care      but you watch it

and      people come by      and someone is
computing his expense account next to you
      and you say to yourself "what place is
this?"      "is this a right place?"      and
 "where am i going in this right place?"
      somehow im over kansas      and you look
down and you say "this must be kansas because
thats how long ive been travelling"      but
 you cant see kansas      what you see are
rifts in clouds and you wonder "what place is
that under there?"      it doesnt have a big
label      i know that john baldessari went a-
round california marking the letters "C"
"A" "L" "I" "F" "O" "R" "N" "I" "A" so that
 you could see them from planes      which was
a great service to california      or to psa
      and he took photographs of them later
      and then at least you knew where you
were      if you looked all the time
      though if you lost three letters you
might not know      you might have thought it
was CAFONIA      or you might have forgotten
each letter as you came to the next one
      but the point is youd have a chance to
figure it out      but i kept wondering where
i was going      in coming to philadelphia
      there was something of a question      i
would never go to the rodin museum again
      no hostility involved      its just that
no reason in the world      that im now aware
of would bring me to look at another rodin
      and i kept saying to myself "what am i
going to do in philadelphia?"      "im going
 to talk about duchamp?      no      im not going to talk about duchamp when i get there
      thats the last thing in my mind to talk
about when i get to philadelphia      is to
 talk once again about duchamp"      ive written too much about duchamp      duchamp had
talked too much about duchamp      and he was
very careful not to talk too much about duchamp      all his life he spent trying not

to bore people        very carefully not to bore
   people        and now theyre going to make him
   bore people        the institutions are going to
propose that duchamp will be a bore        and he
   hadnt wanted to be a bore        all his life
he kept three quarters of his work hidden
        very carefully so that it could only of-
fend people who deserved to be offended by it
in an appropriate manner        and i felt that
he had a right        to the obscurity he had
   claimed for parts of his work        and to the
crankiness he had claimed for other parts of
   his work        and im going to protect that
   but thats another lecture another talk
        another poem        and thats what i propose
to do tomorrow but        im coming here i realized        im coming to a college        now colleges are not all the same        and an art college        is not the same as any other
   and i teach in a place i teach in a college        in california        and        the people
who come to colleges are        there with expectations        some kind of expectations
        theres a transient quality to a college
        youre there hoping for some        change
of status        that is        youre there in some
preparational state        and its not entirely
clear what        teaching in a college is either
   as far as im concerned its neither clear
what teaching in a college is        nor is it
   clear what learning in a college is        or
attending a college is        im older than most
   people who go to colleges        most not all
        younger than others        but the fact is
        i once went to college        and i keep try-
ing to think of that when i teach in a college
        because teaching in college is something
   for me        of an inquiry        that is a way of
trying to find something        or trying to find
a way to something        which may help other
   people find a way to something        because
ive been to other places before them        and

itll turn out they go to other places than the
places i intended to go        there is a terrible problem        the notion of a teacher
    is that experience will help you        you
know?        and there is a terrible lurking
fear        in my mind        and ive always had
this fear        that experience prepares you for
what will never happen again        and its a
terrible challenge        to anybody who has experience        to find out what its worth
    you know it must be worth something
        and i think its worth something        i
dont think its worth nothing        on the other
hand im very nervous about what it is that i
    can effectively offer        thats not trivial
    to someone who doesnt have this experi-
ence        thats not also merely boring
    everybody has on occasion been bored by
somebody elses experience        you sit down and
    they tell you "LET ME TELL YOU ..." they
say and you dont want to be told and youre
told and youre told and told and told        and
    ive experienced that too        in college
        although ive experienced other things in
college        i kept saying to myself "what is
it about a college        that is the most ex-
        perience-like experience of it?"        i mean
there are a lot of things in life that are
not experiences        you dont regard them as
    experiences        you go through them and you
say "that wasnt an experience        that wasnt
    an experience        that was an experience!"
    in fact everybody has some notion as to
what is an experience and what is not an experience        and a lot of it has to do with what
you think is either beneficial or real        it
doesnt have to be beneficial        it might just
simply be real        and your definition of the
real has a lot to do with your notion of
what an experience should be        because your
definition of the real is more like a hope
    about things that should prove to be real

the real is like a construction      something that you build      piece by piece
      and then it falls on you      or you move
into it      and then youre sorry      or youre
delighted      you built a house out of it and
you moved into it and then you furnished the
house      well the ambiguity of this act
      of constructing the real      is something
that i wanted to talk about      because its
an art question as much as a life question
      though its not obligatory that we make it
an art question      when i moved to california i came from new york      which is a great
thriving enclave of activity      there were
millions of people all around and most of
them seem to have been artists      of some
sort or another      maybe i was mistaken but
it seemed to me there were all sorts of artists
      there were many more artists than there
were audiences      which was all right      artists went to see each others work      and we
were all very excited with everything we were
doing and we were all doing everything      it
seemed      but it became tiring after a
while      very tiring      it was very
friendly      one of the things about new york
that most people dont seem to know about it
is that it was an extraordinarily friendly
place      and pretty soon we got tired of
hearing each others gossip      or each
others work because it was very familiar
and you had the feeling that there was a
world somewhere that wasnt that and that
that world outside it      was not better but
maybe interesting      that one might want
to find out what it was that was not art
      it was as if the walls of new york were
lined with art and you couldnt see anything
but art      the subways were art the streets
were art the actions were art there was nothing that didnt seem to be art-ful      and
overly artful      and everybody was an art

critic      all artists were art critics
        and you looked at something and you said
    "mmm      not bad"      it was getting very ti-
ring      nothing seemed to be at stake in any
    sense      i have to restrain myself      i go
to new york and i see these great subways moving with these concrete poems      paco 135
        rosilda 207      all over the subway sys-
tem with spray paint      and finally there
    arent enough subway cars for these great
art works      and they appear on trees and
rocks      and central park has been taken o-
ver and you expect the whole city to become
one vast art gallery      and though its pleasing its nerve racking      there was some-
    thing very tiring about watching the world
    transformed into art the way you might
watch cows get transformed into hamburger
        and somehow there must be cows that are
not hamburger      so      it was an accident
        i accepted a job in california      it
was really an accident      i mean all my
    life i stood preparing for other things
than what happened to me      i was in the process of taking a doctorate in linguistics and
moonlighting as a curator for an institute of
contemporary art in boston      to which i
commuted      i flew back and forth there during the middle of the week and      i had
all set a career in theoretical linguistics
        a career?      i was interested in theo-
retical linguistics and trained in it
        and someone said to me "how would you
like to take a job teaching art in the university of california?      and you could be
    the curator of our gallery?"      i said
"what would i do in california?      what would
    i teach?"      and he said "youd teach art"
        and i said "wow!      id teach art?
        what art?      any art?      to who?"
        he said "theyre students      they come
regularly      every day students come into

school      they come into school      some of
them bring notebooks      they sit down
and you can talk to them"      and i thought
this was so freaky i said "wow im going to
california"      and i went to california
     we went to california and we moved into
     we drove out      my wife and i      my
wifes an artist      you see theres art all
around      we drove out to california and we
arrived in a nightmarish situation      we arrived in california the day after we came to
   phoenix      we came to phoenix the day andy
warhol was shot      which might have been a-
bout a week after id seen him somewhere
     and that same night      i was about to
check out of our motel      i was standing at
   the checkout desk      ely and blaise were
waiting in the car outside      and i heard a
man saying over and over again in a soft
voice into the telephone "i dont know how it
happened" and it was like a deja vu      like i
was back in benson street in a house in the
bronx we were subletting from a dentist who
was travelling in the far east when we heard
   that john kennedy was shot      and suddenly
     i dont know how      i knew that this
kennedy had been shot too      i had been
watching him on television that evening in the
motel dining room      before the big win in
   california      and now he was shot and we
had this mad scene of driving across the desert      in a world that had just changed
     i didnt know whether andy was dead      and
i didnt know whether kennedy was dead      and
i knew who had shot andy      and i had no i-
dea who had shot kennedy      whom i didnt know
     and i had this      peculiar feeling of
driving across a chaos      and i suppose its
   appropriate that a desert should be a chaos
     that is      the desert that lies between
phoenix arizona and san diego is not a profoundly dangerous or exciting desert anymore

i mean you can get water there and there
are hotdog stands and whatever      but you say
"desert" and it sounds dangerous and exciting
the anza-borrega desert      and it was
at night and it felt like chaos had been re-
stored to that place between arizona and california and it had been repopulated with
monsters      and it was hot when we arrived in
midmorning      having come through the mountain chain skirting the coast      and my little boy got sick      he suddenly threw up and
we had to find a place where there was a doctor because we were a little scared      and
we found a medical center where all the
doctors were out to lunch      and i said to
somebody in a shoestore "what do you do if
somebody gets sick during lunch?"      and
they said "theres a medical center right
up the hill"      and i drove to the medical
center      and there was a medical center
in california a medical center is unlike
anything youve ever seen      unless youre a
californian      medical centers depend on redwood trees      because theyre made out of
redwood trees and iceplant      because what
they do is level off an area      whatever was
there they take a bulldozer and level it off
if there were eucalyptus trees they knock
them down they push things out of the way
and then what they dont cover with redwood and blacktop they cover with iceplant
wherever you go theres iceplant      its
a kind of squushy water-retaining plant
that flowers very prettily      its a bizarre
plant and its rubbery and it forms a lawn
all over southern california      and no matter what you do southern california is charac-
terized by iceplant      it grows like crazy
normally there would be a coastal desert
but there is this iceplant      and
theres the medical center      and the medical

center has these large open spaces cooled by
  rooflike structures that are not exactly
  rooves      theyre strips of redwood that
cast shade wherever they go        and there are
  these genteel offices      sometimes with
  muzak      and theres nobody in the offices
      that is        there are a few people around
      a nurse or a clerk        but theres nobody
  there      its lunchhour      and you say
"whats going on?       i mean here i am in california and i cant find a doctor"        and they
  say "oh well      its lunch hour"        and i
say "well maybe i can call the university and
find out whats happening"        and i call the
university and nobody answers the phone
      and they say "oh well        theyre closed
  i guess theyre pretty liberal there"
      and i didnt know whether she meant that
they were closed because kennedy was dying and
that that was liberal        or they were liberal
  about lunchhours      i had no way of knowing
      in any event this medical center        which
was a place where a collocation of specialists
  come together in warmth and collegial friend-
liness       is a place called a medical center
      and there was in this medical center a
man called a dentist        a strange morose man
      into whose office nobody ever came
      i went there once        and i felt i had
made a mistake        he felt i had made a mistake        he had been sitting there looking out
  of his window at the iceplant and now he
  looked at me as if i was annoying him        now
  he had to stop looking at his iceplant and
  look at my teeth        so he looked disapprov-
ingly at me        as though he was silently
  trying to persuade me to go away        so he
  could go back to looking at his iceplant
      and i went away        and he looked as
  if he felt a bit better        and later i
learned that he had gone away too        that he
was no longer there        and a young man        a
  very beautiful young man        named laurence

riedlinger      a very beautiful young man
came  and took his practice      that is he
 bought his practice      i dont know why he
bought his practice      i was sitting on the
 floor in somebodys house      while the university was erupting      the university was pro-
testing the cambodian war and many of us had
 gone out to visit people to explain why the
university was indignant about the cambodian
venture      or maybe it was the kent state
thing      by now ive forgotten      and i was
 sitting on the floor with other people and
we were talking sanely of why it is that students      the people who come to universi-
ties regularly      found it appalling      and
 there sitting across from me were a lot of
nice people from the town      usually the
 people who were rather pleasant and tolerant and really not appalled about anything
      and there was this very beautiful blond
young man sitting there and he turned out to
 be someone who had come there      to take o-
ver this reluctant dentists practice      and
i couldnt believe it      he was so golden
      handsome      young      gentle      and he
was going to move into this      life      and i
 asked him "what are you doing here?"      he
said he had just graduated from the university of southern california and he had studied
 dentistry there and he had taken over this
 practice      and i saw him a few times
      and he would be sitting there not doing
apparently very much till he got up to clean
 my teeth      and he would go off to tennis
games after he finished cleaning my teeth
      or he would come in from a tennis game
just in time to clean my teeth when i got
 there      and i have a feeling that very few
 people came to this dentist      because
these centers get set up as speculations a-
bout the future population that will yet come
      now there are plenty of people with

toothaches in california and there are plenty of dentists       at least in the areas where
there are plenty of people      but most of the
  people go to the dentists who are overcrowded
      and before you go to a new dentist some
sort of revolution must take place      before
  people come in      in any event he would sit
morosely and he would tell me every time i saw
  him how his life was planned      he had gone
  to school for four years      then he had gone
to dental school      and hed been lucky and
found this practice      and his wife was a
  teacher and she was going to teach for a
  while      till they got a little established
and she could have a baby      and she was a
  beautiful golden child just like him      and
it was very sad      and i would see him every
  year      or every other year      maybe to
get my teeth cleaned      or maybe id run into him in the postoffice or coming out of
the mayfair market      and each year he looked
  older and grayer      and i realized that he
  had prepared this life      he had a terri-
  fically prepared life      and he was waiting
for it to begin      and i kept feeling it
  would be interesting for him to have asked
      if it was the right place for it to begin
      because he was aware that the place he
was at was not the place where it was beginning      and he was waiting for something to
  happen      and i realized that there was
something typical about this thats a students
  problem      this culture develops      a feeling      in one or in ones life      that this
  is not the right place      no matter where
  you are it isnt the right place      because
its not the right time      the whole feeling
  is youre getting ready for something
      youre always getting ready      you know?
      you go off and you      expect to be
  benefited      by something      you go into
school and you take notes      i had one notebook through all my undergraduate career      i

had one notebook that was filled with doodles
and i studied          but i never took anything down with notes          it didnt seem to
make any sense          but i had the notebook
          it gave me a good feeling          that i was
doing something          i used to like the ex-
ercise of writing          and i was there and i
remember that sense that where i was was not
          really a place          that is it was not really
a place it was like a passageway          i had
the feeling i was in a school and it was a
passageway          i had the feeling i was going
to be an artist          of some kind          thats
why im talking about it here          i had the feeling i was going to be an artist but          going
to be an artist was like a whole "going to be"
          and it was all futurity was involved in
this thing          you were getting ready          how
were you getting ready?          what was i going
to get ready to do?          i was going to get ready for something that somebody had already done
          now the one thing about what everybody
had already done is that if you were going to
do it it would be a disaster          the one thing
you cant afford to do is whats already been
done          because its already been done and
done and done and theres nothing meaningful
in doing it all over again          but those were
the 1950s          and the feeling that it was
beneficial to do what everybody had already
done          was all around you          i mean everybody in the 50s knew that what you should do
was only what everybody had already done
          in those days          i remember a friend of
mine          who was taking a course          now
people didnt take courses because they expected to learn something specific          they
werent that naive          i had a friend named
corky          who was taking a course in narra-
tive writing          i think it was called
creative writing but nobody believed that
          it was called narrative writing
          which meant that you wrote stories

and everybody knew what a story was
in those days there was no one who didnt
know what a story was because a story had an
"epiphany"        and you may not know what that
word is       but it was a favorite critical
   term for something that turned things around
        that is       at some point somebody who
had been doing        not very much       realized
   something       when he realized something
   that was the epiphany       it was a very famous type of story       you know it was somehow as if a subtle bolt of lightning hit him
   and he said "wow!"       and it was based on
a reading of james joyces dubliners which were
very popular at that time       naturally
       since it was forty-seven or forty-some
years after theyd been written       they were
a little less popular when they were written
       and with the audience for which they
were written       i said to corky one night
"what are you doing lately?"       he said "what
do you mean?"       "you know" i said "what do
   you do?"       he said "oh       i guess im a
novelist"       i said "why?"       and he said
   "well       because im not writing novels this
year"       he was getting ready to write a novel       he was not writing novels       he was
   preparing to write a novel       you researched
novels       i was going to write a novel then
   too       i dont know why i was going to write
a novel but i had an image of a life as an
artist that had a definitive career       and
a career accumulated       lets say a novelists
   career       how did a novelists career accu-
mulate?       there was an empty bookshelf and
   gradually it filled up with books       your
books       and what you did is you wrote book
one and book two and after a while you had
a lot of books on that bookshelf that were
   by you       and i had an image of what they
looked like       probably a little bit like
   french novels       you know those beautiful
   lemon colored covers and then they became

white colored covers and they were published by
 gallimard     and it was nice     i saw each
one     and the novels would be like by flaubert     well written     because obviously
 they had to be well written     and you would
choose the right words to write them in     because well written novels are always written
in the right words     and youd think a lot
 about those words     youd write 200 words a
   day     150 words a day     but they would
   be the right 150 words     because they
would be better than the other 150 words you
 might have written     and this was a universal thing     it didnt matter whether you
were writing novels or making paintings
     because if you made paintings you made
paintings of that type     that is     you
 knew how a painting was made     and you recognized it by its frame     and inside
of it you had a very clear expectation of
 what would be a good one     and i had a
friend who was learning how to make good ones
     he was working at it     he drew very
well     that is he drew very well in terms
of what they thought drawing was     and he
made marks that looked like things in the
   external world and then     he would blot
   them in certain ways     he would use a wet
paper     and it would look energetic and
     impressionistic     or vaguely picassoid
     in a certain phase of picassos early
 work     and you knew that he was in training
     and he was going to make paintings of
the right sort     after a while     and
later he sure enough did     he went off and
 he got a fulbright to italy     and he
drew monks riding around on motorcycles
     and he added some italianate aspects
to his style     and he came back and became
an illustrator     which had not been his expectation     because his expectation was
that he was going to be an artist     and he

didnt turn out to be an artist      and then
other people turned out to be artists who had
  no such expectation      and thinking back on
this situation of expectation      the question
has become what had we all been doing?    we
  had sat there in these classes      walked
  there through those halls      spent a lot of
time in the cafeteria      probably as much
  time in the cafeteria as we spent anywhere
else       probably it was more beneficial than
  most of the classes      not because of the
food but because there were people who talked
in the cafeteria      it was a conversation
  place      and among these people      there
were a few      contrast people      who didnt
do it that way      by way of endless preparation      i had a friend who suddenly appeared
      his name was gene      gene appeared one
  day      and i dont know how i knew he was a
friend      but i knew it and thats one of the
  things youre sometimes more certain about
  when youre younger than when youre older
      anyway he suddenly appeared and he said
to me "look ive made these paintings      cmon
   i want you to look at my paintings im an
artist"      and this was very bold and was
  very unlike anything that happened in a
college cafeteria in the 1950s      he said
"look at my paintings      what do you think
of them?"      he said "come up to my loft and
  look at my paintings"      so i went to his
  loft and looked at his paintings      and i
dont know exactly what i thought of them
      it didnt too much matter      it was in-
teresting that someone should come to me and
say "these are my paintings" not like "im
  training to be a painter"      i was sort of
  shocked      and he said "well what do you
  think of them" and i said "they look energetic      why do you draw that way?"      you
  know?      and he said "de kooning likes them"
      i said "well      thats nice      whos de

kooning?"      i didnt know who de kooning
was      that was a mistake      soon i found
 out      and gene took himself very seriously
    which was unlike a student      and he
went to a philosophy class      and it was
a gentle      genteel philosophy class      in
 ethics      and he came around      im not sure
whether he was registered for the class or not
      i think he used to go around the school
looking for things he might be interested in
and it was a class taught by a sweet man
      a vaguely friendly left wing      grey
haired man who smoked a pipe      and thought
      ethics      and somehow somewhere in the
middle of the class gene was beginning to get
 nervous      because we were talking about
the things that might lead people to hold
certain values      or the professor was talking about that      and it was beginning to
   look like we were      weighing things
and you had six pounds of value and six
 pounds of negative value and      you put
them in the scale and      before you knew it
      you made a decision      that is      its
a tossup      or its not a tossup      its better to kill your mother than to die      or its
   worse to kill your mother than to die      and
gene suddenly bristled and he said to the
professor "what about the unconditioned?"
 and the professor said "what      what do you
 mean?"      gene repeated "what about the
 unconditioned?      what about that which has
 no conditioned grounds?"      and the professor just repeated "what do you mean?"
      and gene simply shook his head and said
"being is one"      now while this may seem
a little absurd it was very serious and quite
 simple      gene didnt want to be had by all
 this weighing      because weighing in this
way is endless      and even for the professor
  who professed it      it would not yield a
decision      not a real decision      and the
 professor      who was really a very intelli-

gent man       and might have known this
     was just otherwise oriented       and said
to him "what do you mean 'being is one'?
     what could that possibly mean?"       being
a reasonable man       he didnt want to hear
'being is one'       unless you provided him
 with a reasonable position on 'being is one'
     and gene said 'well       the ontological
quality is unitary"       they couldnt talk together       as you might have expected       they
had very little they could say to each other
     and they were both valuable people
     they both were pursuing their possibili-
ties       and we in the class       felt as hos-
tages       to something else       which was happening       for a moment       as if the real
world had appeared       by accident       in our
midst       without preparation
          now       preparing to do something
   clearly you can imagine the virtues of
preparing something       i mean i can imagine
  the virtues of preparing       of becoming
something that you aim to be       of readying
something that you aim to do       you start out
 to do some thing       i worked very long on a
  novel       that was when i was doing novels
     now i dont do novels       i do other kinds
   of things       but i was preparing to do
something that had a name       which was a novel       and i said to myself "im going to do
this 'novel' and the 'novel' is going to be
'about something'"       and i didnt have to worry what it was going to be about       that was
given       it wasnt conditioned       i knew
what the novel was going to be about       the
 novel was about a girl who got the stigmata
 or sort of got the stigmata       and i didnt
  know how i came to think about this       the
girl who was going to get the stigmata       but
  i did       and i knew other things about this
girl       like she had one brown eye and one
 blue eye       and i dont know how i knew she

had one brown eye and one blue eye or that she
was 12 or 13 years old except     that she was
having a conversation on the beach with a-
nother girl and that she was walking up the
beach toward me when she suddenly looked up
and i saw that she had one brown eye and one
blue     and she was staying in rockaway in
the summer of 1945 when tokyo was being bombed
by firebombs     and earlier in that year an
airplane had flown into the empire state building leaving a great gaping hole in its side
     and all of this made some kind of sense
     and she got involved with some people
     other kids slightly older     and they
had a beach party     and a slightly crippled
slightly drunken older black man came by
     and began talking to them·     and he was
coming on that he was a choctaw indian
     while they were getting him drunker and
drunker     and they didnt believe it
     they thought he was coming on     and
they kept getting him drunker and drunker
     and they kept taunting him and teasing
him     about how could he be a choctaw indian     they had never seen a choctaw indian
either     but what they really meant was
"youre just an old broken down black man with
a limp     and while we dont know what a
choctaw indian would look like     he wouldnt
look like you"     but they didnt really have
the nerve to say that right out to him     in
case he was maybe dangerous or something
     so they kept asking him for some signs
     or some special knowledge that would
prove to them that he was really a choctaw
indian     to talk choctaw or dance an indian dance or something     and he got madder
and madder and finally he got mad enough to
get up and try to dance     and because he
was pretty drunk and had a bad leg he started
stumbling around and weaving and limping
     while they laughed harder and harder

till he suddenly jumped way up in the air
and      let out a weird scream and came down
dancing and singing on his bad leg as if there
was nothing wrong with it at all       and yelling a long and unintelligible string of syl-
lables that sounded like it must have been
something from the way he sang them       and if
anybody knew it       it was choctaw       and was
about how the earth shook and the sun went
black as a veil of hair dropped in front of
it and the moon turned blood red while the
stars fell out of the sky like fruit out of
a tree shaken by a big wind       which for con-
noisseurs of the matter was a choctaw translation of the book of revelation       and he
collapsed in a heap and they stuck him in a
lifeguard tower with a bottle in his hand and
ran away       i had all this worked out in my
mind       but the preparation       i had a series of images       but to prepare a novel
a novel was made like flaubert       the
way flaubert made life       the way flaubert
made love       flaubert made love       he went
and found a girl and then he went back home
and wrote her letters       and flaubert was
particularly well advised in this       the
two "lovers" corresponded and the letters
became a "love life"       the way the novels
were turned out       a paragraph a day
the notion was that you prepare the well
made block       novels were sculpture       they
were carved       you went chip       chip
chip       off marble       there may be all
kinds of sculpture       but what you had in
mind was marble       whatever it looked like
it was marble for sure       and i had five sections       and in one section somebody had to
take a train trip down to north carolina and
had to cross over the chesapeake bay       and
i took a train over the chesapeake bay to find
out what the trip was like in order to prepare to write a novel that had very little

to do with the trip across the chesapeake bay
because what you did with novels was you
prepared them      you were always getting ready      the idea of getting ready was based on
the feeling that you were never at the right
place      that wherever you were it was not
the right place      like the whole of salammm-
bo      whatever you had to do      it was always going to be done in an other way
and the other way would become a way you
would become capable of      because you had
arrived at an other place      the right place
that was the right place      and you always wondered where the right place precisely was      but that was the nature of schooling
was to prepare you with the notion that
eventually there would be the right place
you would issue forth from the last day
of graduate school and suddenly find yourself
in the right place      now i had a very long
undergraduate career      i seemed to major
in about eighteen different things and
i was not prepared to be issued forth
from the university      in fact i had my sixth
year program well in hand      and i forget
what i was majoring in that year      it may
have been physiological psychology or some
such thing      and i arrived with my beautiful program of classes      which i was getting for nothing      so it didnt bother me
city college in new york was free      and
i had a very good job working as an engineer
in a bubble gum factory      designing machinery for them      and      a totally absurd
job      and i had never expected to do that
either      but that wasnt the right place
and i didnt take it too seriously      because
there we were in this bubble gum factory
trying to determine how it was that a child
who paid a penny      for bubble gum      would
get both parts of the joke      and they
would prove to be the right parts      so that

if it should say in the first frame "why did
the chicken cross the road?"      it should
say in the second "to get to the other side"
   as opposed say      to the child opening
up his one cent bubble gum and it saying "to
get to the other side      who was that lady
i saw you with last night?"      because the
strip came off a continuous roll      and lo
if the blade cut in the wrong place      the
child would be defrauded of at least one
half of his reward      that is      the cavi-
ties he would get anyway      but he wouldnt
   get the joke      so this was not part of my
preparation      that was subsidiary and accidental      and there was the central career
   and i walked in with my program for a
physiological psychological major or whatever
it was and they said to me "you have graduated"      and i said "i have graduated?      how
   could i have graduated?      i didnt take
   hygiene 71"      they said "you have graduated      graduated"      and i said "graduated?"      they said "yes      we will accept
zoology 32      as hygiene 71"      i said "but
   it isnt      i dont know all about those sex
practices you describe in hygiene 71      ill
never know and ill be sent out into the world
   whereas all ill know about will be the various nervous systems of the vertebrates"
      and they said "no      no      no      you-
ve graduated"      i said "i havent had
math 61"      and they said "math 61 is elemen-
   tary mathematics      youve had the theory of
complex functions      out!"      and there i
was      not that i couldnt support myself
      id been supporting myself since i was
sixteen      but i wasnt prepared for being issued forth from this      preparational device
   this institutional preparation device
      i really wasnt ready for it      i didnt
know what i was going to do      what was i
going to do with my life?      what do you mean
"what was i going to do with my life?"      i

was doing it all along     and there was something bizarre about this     i hadnt the
 faintest idea of what i was going to do
       and i was doing it all along     but i
 felt i wasnt doing it     it was very important
 to realize i wasnt doing it     no matter what
   i was doing was not it     and i kept saying
   to myself "why isnt it it?"     because i
 wasnt quite sure     i wasnt sure what the
 "it" was that was "it"     but i knew when it
   wasnt there     that is     "ill know it
 when i come to it" was the feeling i had of it
       "ill know it when i discover it"     it
 will suddenly be revealed to me     it would
   be something like a calling     a friend of
 mine had gone to a divinity school on a scho-
 larship     and he had not had a calling
           his sense of vocation was not there
       and he was worried about it     in those
 days they took things like that more seriously
       its not that long ago it was in the 1950s
       its when wagner college was still a luthe-
 ran school     and he had spoken to them about
 it but they didnt want to discuss it     they
   wanted him to go through     "dont worry a-
 about having a calling     it will come to
 you"     and he felt very sad about it     e-
 ventually he dropped out of divinity school
 because he didnt have a calling     so there
 was this sense that you would have a calling
   and the calling would come after long training     now at some point     i had the feeling     and i dont know why i had this feeling
       that always i had been doing everything
 just the same     that all the things i had
   been doing i had been doing     and that
 comes as a tremendous and transformational
 shock     that i had not been writing novels
   but i had been writing something     that
 i had not been making paintings but i had
 been making some kind of art     i had been
   doing certain kinds of photographing say
 and making certain kinds of sound tracks

and doing some kinds of performances
which i had thought would be getting
me ready to do something else      and they
didnt get me ready      and then i was doing
researching      and it turned out that the
researching itself was something      i had
been studying things      and the studying
was itself something      for no reason      the
studying was itself interesting      and then
i began to realize i could do anything i
wanted      and this was odd      because id
always been doing everything i wanted
nobody had ever stopped me from doing
everything i wanted since high school
which had in fact been a prison      im
sure it was a prison      high school was such a
prison that nobody did what he wanted      the
high school system of america      as i remember it      was a penal institution
and i went to a very good one      it was
a boys high school in new york      called
brooklyn technical high school      which
had 5800 boys      which is a very large
number of boys      and really a rather foolish arrangement      probably it was arranged
that way because in those days      they
thought only boys would become engineers
and since they arranged for only boys to
go there      only boys became engineers from
there      but most of the boys who went
through there didnt become engineers anyway
thats fairly sure      and most of the
people there walked around in a state of
walls      that is      they had the feeling
there were always walls around them      so
much so that i remember seeing a situation in
in that school because the rules were very
mad      i remember seeing a situation in the
lunchroom      where a fierce quarrel broke
out      you know      boys schools are always very buggy      probably because there are
no girls there      among other things      but
also because of the rules      and there was

this fierce hostility that developed between
   these two guys      and one guy      unable
to contain himself dropped his tray and hit
   the other one      and the other      who was
   not afraid of him      looked at the first
one and said      "not here"      where then?
         outside      after school      behind in
   the park      because there was a rule in the
school      the school had created its rule
      so much so that his survival itself was
affected by his sense that this was not the
   right place      and this inability to take
   things seriously      this strange sense that
you cant take seriously anything that is at
hand      is one of the great weaknesses of the
   theory of preparation      now i dont believe
that you never have to prepare things      it
may be that you have to prepare things
         maybe you do      because i can think of
cases where not preparing things      or the
lack of time you have for preparation can become a disaster      i had a friend      who
was writing      he was in college with me
      and john was trying to write      i wont
say novels      ill say about human experience
      why call it a novel?      lets get simp-
ler      he was trying to talk about human
experience      writing is a form of fossilized
   talking      which gets put inside of a can
      called a book      and i respect that
can      its a means of preservation      or
   maybe we should say in a frozen food container called a book      but on the other hand
if you dont know how to handle that frozen
food container that icy block will never turn
   back into talking      and if it will never
turn back into talking it will never be of
any use to you again      so lets not call it a
   novel      lets say he wanted to do some kind
   of talking about human experience      and
and john molle was thinking about human experienc

when he came down with a disease      and the
disease he came down with      he came down
with some tumor in his leg      and he dropped
out of school      and the state of pain that
  he was in made it very difficult for him to
think about human experience      except the
  experience of pain      which was really a
rather special experience      even if it was
  universal      besides which it was not the
experience he had started out by being interested in      and he had the leg amputated
      and he had disappeared from our lives
        and i remember      we were in touch with
him      friends of mine and i      but it was a
difficult kind of "in touch"      he was in a
hospital and      then he was at home in new
  jersey      and we were in new york      and
we went out to visit him on several occasions
        and i remember      at one point      visi-
ting him in his home      and he started to
talk to us      about      life      about what
  he thought life was      and he only had the
life he had      and he was enshrouded by very
  heavy pain      and sometimes drugs      and
he was inhibited      he couldnt get around
 much      he didnt walk around much      because he was on crutches when he was able
to walk at all      and he was overridden by
a kind of      he was only nineteen      and he
 had this kind of walled in sexiness      and
  pain      that was all there together      and
he started telling us this long story
        now what was this long story he was
      telling us?      he told us about how he
had been reading this novel by arthur koestler
        and hed been trying to read it and in the
book there was this man who became a prisoner
and hed had this girl friend      and how
their lovemaking was built on a kind of intense
  mechanical conditioning      and how lovingly
   they went over the details of their physical preparations      and how when he      the
lover      lying on top of his girl friend and

holding her under the arms pressed with his
     thumb on her nipple she came        and john
was fascinated with this and said how it
made him think about how nobody ever talked
about the real experience         of masturba-
tion        and we all felt uncomfortable
     not because we thought there was any-
thing that was such a big deal about mastur-
bation       and he kept talking about it
     in this great physical detail       he said
"no one has ever described       the subtle
transformation of feeling       the casual
  brushing of       maybe some alien surface
     against the tender skin of the penis
     and from this       diffuse pleasure
     about as interesting as an itch      with
the hand coming back to stroke       like a
lover       the interested part       and how this
will shift from a gentle aura       where its
still always possible to turn back       with
a flush of pleasure       to a fierce and growing
concentration pointed by the intense and sys-
tematic stroking by the fingers of the distended and trembling crown       then the release"               and we all got very
nervous       we said "yeah"       and there was
a wall of silence       we had nothing to say
     and it was a real experience       it was
a human experience       it was just       very
walled in       he was in the right place
     that is       he was in the only place he
was       now what was he going to do?
     write about it as a way of living?
     is there a way of writing about it or
talking about it       i dont know       i dont
 know what there is to talk about that will
get beyond the walls of that small room
     maybe it will maybe it wouldnt       i dont
know       "will" is not the issue       because
in the end he didnt write it       in the end
there was a combination of eroticism and mor-
phine       and then we got a small black card

in the mail that he had died and we went to his
 funeral         and i remember going to his funeral      i remember driving out there with
     a wagnerian heldentenor named friedrich
 bonhoffer       who was a friend of his         and
i went out there and another friend went out
 there        and we drove out to this bleak ita-
lian funeral in new jersey         where i remember
 all the elderly ladies in black dresses and
 those funny shoes        and john molle had evaporated        it was totally impossible to recognize where john molle was in this         sicilian
 funeral        and there it was        a grouping
around a kind of        evaporated grave        and
on the way back        i remember        for a while
 everybody was very quiet because we had nothing we could say        and suddenly bonhoffer
     who was driving        this immense helden-
tenor who was driving this tiny broken-down
volkswagen that was being held together like
 with rubber bands and chewing gum        started
 singing        and at first he started singing
somewhat gently        but in his full bellowing
 voice        these swelling wagnerian arias
     and in the beginning we were nervous
     but then we also started to sing with him
     and as we began to run out of wagner
we somehow started in on a series of silly
filthy german songs        bonhoffer roaring at
 the top of his lungs        tears were rolling
down this huge germans face as he bellowed
 out "amanda mach' die beine breit        der
kaiser braucht soldaten"        then in bonhof-
fers house        we were eating this goddam vile
german cheese        a brown reeking cheese
     a foul smelling oily marvelous tasting
 cheese        as bonhoffer sat in this easy
 chair        reading to us from a book that
he had somehow picked up        it was a book
 written by alfred de musset        a lunatic
genteel book about making out with nuns in
a monastery        and that was also a place

and it was closer to johns place        that
we had somehow been unable to find        it was
how somehow we couldnt find the right place
        and pornography is all about inauspicious-
    ness and preparation also        one of the main
    things about pornography is that its involved
with finding the right place        with preparations and litanies        you recite litanies
    you know a pornographic movie is something
    like the recitation of a text        there is a
naming of parts        and a naming of acts
        and the recitation itself becomes a kind
    of incantation in order to arrive at some
place        which is in fact called "coming"
        the point is that youre arriving        the
aim is        arrival        now i can understand
    places that are not considered        the place
        and the necessity for a litany        the
    necessity for a litany is based on the recog-
nition        of unpreparedness        and the need
    for preparation        that has sometimes a
    justification        the inauspiciousness of
being unprepared        as one may be unprepared
    or insufficiently prepared        i can imagine
    being unprepared for many things        it may
    be though        that the litany doesnt get you
    better prepared at all        it just takes you
to a different place        and it may be the
    characteristic of being an artist        and
maybe that means of being human        though im
    not sure about that        maybe it is that
the characteristic of an artist is the gift
    of being ready to do something for which youre
    not prepared        i have never been ready for
    anything i have ever done at all        ive never
had the sense of being adequately prepared for
    it        its always arrived too early        it
    should have arrived later        or then it comes
late        and you were lucky        you werent
    preparing for it and something else happened
        and you decided that that was it        the
    decision that what has happened by accident

might be it      is a decision that winds up
 being made by artists all the time      how
do you know when youre through with something?
     you know because the phone rang      as
somebody once pointed out      and then you
 cant ever get back to it again and its as
ready as it will ever be      because theres
 no reason to go on      the telephone rang
      why not?      now i might say of this
particular discourse      that theres no place
 at which i can end it      without producing
 a kind of profoundly pornographic poetic effect      which i assure you i can do      i
 could produce a vast symphonic conclusion
     and you might walk out feeling benefited
 but i wont do it

            for the last couple of years ive been
         working at "talk poems"      because i see
         all poetry as some kind of talking
              which is some kind of thinking
           and because ive never liked the idea of
         going into a closet to address myself over
         a typewriter      what kind of talking is
         that?      ive gotten into the habit of
          going to some particular place      with
         something on my mind      but with no par-
         ticular words in my mouth      seeking
         a particular occasion      to talk to parti-
         cular people in a way i hope is valuable
         for all of us      since the moore college
         of art in philadelphia was kind enough to
          invite me "is this the right place?" was
         composed and performed there on october 30
          1973      because it was worked out with no
         sense of a page in mind the text is not prose
            which is      as i see it      "concrete
         poetry with justified margins"      it is
         a notation or score of an oral poem
             with margins consequently unjustified

                          da

# FIVE POEMS

MARICHIKO

*Translated by Kenneth Rexroth*

1

Who is there? Me.
Me who? I am me, you are you.
But you take my pronoun,
And we are us.

*Dare ga iruno? Watashi.*
*Watashi te dare? Watashi wa watashi, anata wa anata.*
*Demo anata wa watashi ni tatte*
*Futari wa watashitachi ni naru.*

2

I wish I could be
Kannon of the thousand heads
To kiss you and Kannon
Of the thousand arms

To embrace you, and
Dainichi to hold you
Forever.

*Kannon Bosatsu naraba*
*Sen no kuchibiru de anata ni kuchizukeshi,*
*Sen no tede anata wo aibu dekiruno ni,*
*Soshite Dainichi Nyorai ni natte*
*Eien ni*
*Anata wo dakishimete itai.*

3

I cannot forget
The perfumed dusk inside the
Tent of your black hair
As we woke to make love
After a long night of love.

*Watashi niwa wasurerarenai*
*Nagai ai no yoru no ato*
*Futatabi ai ni mezameta toki no*
*Kurokami ni oo arete honoguraku*
*Kosui no ka wo todomeru ano temaku wo.*

4

Every morning
I wake alone, dreaming
My arm is your sweet flesh
Pressing my lips.

*Maiasa mezameruto tada hitori,*
*Kono ude watashino kuchioiru wo*
*Oshitsukeru Anata no kanbi na*
*Karada dattano wa yume no naka.*

5

I hold your head tight
Between my thighs and press
Against your mouth and
Float away forever in
An orchid boat
On the River of Heaven.

*Anata no atama wo watashi no*
*Mata ni shikkari hasami*
*Anata no kuchi ni watashio tsuyoku*
*Oshitsukeru to, watashi wa*
*Ran no hana no fune ni notte*
*Tokoshie ni Tengoku no Kawa wo*
*Tadayotte yuku.*

# FOUR POEMS

DENISE LEVERTOV

## IN THAI BINH (PEACE) PROVINCE

*for Muriel and Jane*

I've used up all my film on bombed hospitals,
bombed village schools, the scattered
lemon-yellow cocoons at the bombed silk-factory,

and for the moment all my tears too
are used up, having seen today
yet another child with its feet blown off,
                a girl, this one, eleven years old,
patient and bewildered in her home, a fragile
small house of mud bricks among rice fields.

So I'll use my dry burning eyes
to photograph within me
dark sails of the river boats,
warm slant of afternoon light
apricot on the brown, swift, wide river,
village towers—church and pagoda—on the far shore,
and a boy and small bird both
perched, relaxed, on a quietly-grazing
buffalo.      Peace within the
         long war.

It is that life, unhurried, sure, persistent,
I must bring home when I try to bring
the war home.
                    Child, river, light.

Here the future, fabled bird
that has migrated away from America,
nests, and breeds, and sings,

common as any sparrow.

                              (Hanoi, Fall 1972)


ROOM

                                        *for D. Mitchell and D. Hass*

Shelf of worn, chipped, exquisite china oddments,
for daily use.
Baskets, for fruit, potatoes, shopping.
Stove with grill where David
makes such good brown toast.
Left of the sink, above the counter,
Mary Wollstonecraft, fair face, dark shadows, energy.
Slightly unsteady, the small table. Notes to each other,
and soon, when David and David come home,
strong cups of tea.
It's the kitchen, its window viewless,
and not the handsome calm of the living room,
I find myself in, at peace,
though the presence across the hall of
*that* room too is part of being here:
the threadbare gracious carpet,
surreal romances of the Victorian *découpage* screen,
poplars and oaks and sunsets the large windows look to.
Afternoon, an ample easy quiet.
                              But it breaks
sharply: the Davids

have moved, all the objects
stand at new angles, a kitchen I've never seen,
light from another compass point.
This room, my refuge, is nowhere but in my mind,
more blurred for them than for me, their memories
too many to sift and focus. 'Bees of the invisible,'
take this nectar, transform it, internalize it! If I lose
the knowledge of this place,
my soul shall be diminished. There is a song in all
humankind, that rooms, houses, parks, streets, fields
and particular corners of fields, rivers and certain
eye-span reaches of rivers, are notes in, as people are.
Give me the power
to sound this note, the disappeared-
as-if-torn-down, but clear, cool, tranquil kitchen
on Downside Crescent present in me,
a place to *be* in, not pretending
no tears were shed in it, no hard words ever shouted,
no grey mornings ever caught in the small mirror over the sink
but seeing despite that, precisely because of that,
(grief not being turned away, a place
made for grief to be) one could
*be* there, and breathe easy, uncrowded.
A note or chord of notes
sustained, hushing, recurrent
in the stream of the song.


'THE POEM RISING BY ITS OWN WEIGHT'

> *'The poet is at the disposal of his night.'*
> —*Cocteau*

The singing-robes fly onto your body and cling there silkily,
you step out on the rope and move unfalteringly across it,

and seize the fiery knives unscathed and
keep them spinning above you, a fountain
of rhythmic rising, falling, rising
flames,

and proudly let the chains
be wound about you, ready
to shed them, link by steel link,
padlock by padlock—

                  but when your graceful
confident shrug and twist drives the metal
into your flesh and the cobra grip of it tightens
and you see rust on the chains and blood in your pores
and you roll
over and down a steepness into a dark hole
and there is not even the sound of mockery in the distant air
somewhere above you where the sky was,
no sound but your own breath panting:

then it is that the miracle
walks in, on his swift feet,
down the precipice straight into the cave,
opens the locks,
knots of chain fall open,
twists of chain unwind themselves,
links fall asunder,
in seconds there is a heap of scrap
metal at your ankles, you step free and at once
he turns to go—

but as you catch at him with a cry,
clasping his knees, sobbing your gratitude,
with what radiant joy he turns to you,
and raises you to your feet,
and strokes your dishevelled hair,
and holds you,
          holds you,
               holds you
close and tenderly before he vanishes.

# THE WAY IT IS

More real than ever, as I move
in the world, and never out of it,
Solitude.

Typewriter, telephone, ugly names
of things we use, I use. Among them, though,
float milkweed silks.

Like a mollusk's, my hermitage
is built of my own cells.
Burned faces, stretched horribly,

eyes and mouths forever open,
weight the papers down on my desk.
No day for years I have not thought of them.

And more true than ever the familiar image
placing love on a border
where, solitary, it paces, exchanging
across the line a deep attentive gaze
with another solitude pacing there.

Yet almost no day, too, with no
happiness, no
exaltation of larks uprising from the heart's
peatbog darkness.

# HOW THE COMB GIVES
# A FRESH MEANING TO THE HAIR

WALTER ABISH

### The roads

Some of the roads of Albuquerque permit the people to view the fine scenery from outside the city. The Pueblo Indians used to build roads that dissolved in the vastness of what lay outside of their experience. With a detachment quite unknown to the late settlers of Albuquerque, the Indians observe the growing Albuquerque network of roads until its grid system finally encompasses "The Brook of the Running Spirit," and splits into two "The Mountain That Is Too Hot to Touch." Now and then a new road will provide a visitor access to a museum. Now and then a road will also launch a new cabbie. . . There are already far too many cabbies stationed in front of the Albuquerque railroad station. There are also far too many cabbies blocking the roads, blocking with their battered vehicles what the Pueblo Indians describe as "The Elsewhereness of Things." The cabbies won't budge until their demands are met. But they suffer from poor leadership. They also suffer from a lack of public sympathy. They are not retarded, at least not according to the prevailing medical standard, and therefore cannot expect to elicit sympathy for their plight.

*The children*

The retarded children have managed to live through another hot summer. They are now staying among the Indians in a pueblo that is less than an hour's drive from Albuquerque. The terrible events that took place on the blocked roads just outside of Albuquerque have not marred their memories. They have emerged unscathed by the experience. In any event, they are still considered as being sacred by the Indians, who have taught them to make ceremonial masks and weave baskets for the tourist trade. Following the events that have been described in some detail in a voluminous eight-volume work entitled *The Remembrance of Albuquerque,* the children traveled in a Greyhound bus, flew in a helicopter, and on one unforgettable occasion sailed on a yacht on the Potomac. This was on the occasion of their visit to the capital to receive the Medal of Merit for Retarded Children. A memento of their visit is a large wall-sized map of Washington. Back in their small adobe and stone house in the pueblo, the map hangs on the wall of their playroom. They do not yet understand the meaning of the map. The map, in their minds, resembles a sand drawing for a ceremonial Navaho dance. How can they, existing as they do in a state of retardation, distinguish a network of streets from a network of elaborate mythological destinations.

*The comb*

The comb parts the hair and exposes sections of the white scalp underneath. The comb gives a fresh meaning to the hair. It serves as an indicator. It provides a sort of explanation. The comb is made of plastic, but in the children's retarded hands this hard resilient material is kneaded into a softer and more rubbery substance resembling the unparalleled softness of their faces.

*Names (1)*

The retarded children have names. They do not always remember their names. They do not, consequently, always respond to their names. . . They are not even sure what a name is meant to be. They are called: Harry, John, Dwight, Lyndon, Dick, Frank, Bess, Jackie,

Minnie, Lady, Pat, and Eleanor. In themselves the names do not with any specificity indicate the nature of their abnormality. The Pueblo Indians are convinced that their abnormality is sacred, and that everything that is related to the children is equally sacred. The children's names are listed on their medical reports and on their birth certificates. The certificates are stamped: RETARDED. The children and the Pueblo Indians take sacredness for granted.

## Mrs. Dip

Mrs. Dip arrived in Albuquerque three years ago. Her first name is Clara. Naturally, she visited the Pueblo Indians, and examined their weary faces. She also climbed the tall wood ladders that lead into their ceremonial chambers by herself, quite unafraid, somehow radiating a purity and confidence. It came as no surprise to anyone when the town council by a unanimous vote elected Mrs. Dip to work with the poor retarded children who had been left in the care of the city fathers.

## Marriage

Even the retarded children cheered when Mrs. Dip said: I do. They now formed a nuclear family. The ceremony was a simple one. Mrs. Dip walking barefoot down the aisle to be purified by the priest, as the children knelt and the Pueblo Indians in their ceremonial robes danced outside. The event, like so many of the events that are to follow, has been preserved on slides. Mrs. Dip at first failed to understand what the Indians meant when they spoke of the children's sacredness. But she is finding out. . . Shall we have a barbecue tonight, asked Mr. Dip. Yes darling, she answered, thinking, this is the bliss I've always wanted to experience.

## Glass

Mrs. Dip is only twenty-four. Her young shining face is visible through the windshield. The shatterproof windshield increases the distance between her and the retarded children who are clamoring for her attention, for her love, for her unbearably sweet embraces.

They have grown accustomed to being caressed by her. But once inside her car Mrs. Dip is unapproachable. Sadly the children stand on the promontory of the pueblo and watch her drive away in a cloud of dust. It is the sweeping cloud of the spirit, say the Pueblo Indians, consoling the children.

Each day Mrs. Dip drives from a small suburb of Albuquerque to the pueblo. In order to reach the pueblo she drives across a narrow bridge spanning a canyon. She and the few other drivers who have business at the pueblo drive at a snail's pace, because the bridge is old and unsafe. At the other end of the bridge the children are waiting to dribble their saliva on her freshly starched blouse. They are waiting to scrutinize her carefully, to examine her wardrobe, to register every nuance of change, every minute alteration.

## Fingernails

Her fingernails are painted a bright red. The bright red shatters the already tense atmosphere of expectation. Mrs. Dip may not be aware of it, but to the children her hands are sending out signals which they are trying very hard to interpret. The reasoning behind this is simple. If they can comprehend what she is saying with her hands, they may, in the future, be able to understand the other more intimate signals of her slim and sweet body. The children, naturally, have spotted her bright red fingernails and become unusually unruly. Mrs. Dip hurriedly enters the small room on her left, and firmly closes the door, locking it on the inside. A hush falls over the children. Mrs. Dip has disappeared from sight. Is she in the peeing room? Is she in the Pueblo Indian room of the running water dance, or has she somehow become invisible? They strain their ears, listening for the sound of running water, and dare they hope, for the sound of something else, the intimate sound, the distant sound of Mrs. Dip's body dissolving.

## The city

It is built on a large mirrorlike surface. The streets are polished daily. The people avoid looking at the ground in order not to be blinded by the sun. When Marcel Proust first entered the city he did not know where the center was located. He spoke the language but had great difficulty in making himself understood. There are cracks in the mirrorlike surface, but these are carefully disguised. When Marcel first arrived he was particularly struck by the cleanliness and the silence.

Have you come here to study the Pueblo Indians, he was asked, or do you, instead, wish to write about the retarded children?

## Marcel's childhood

In volume one of his great work of fiction, Marcel Proust described a few intimate details of his childhood. He also described his dependence upon his mother. In general, the people he described spent most of their time in sitting rooms. They frequently spoke about their travels, past and future. They compared different cities, cities he had never seen. Like him, all of them were pale. Like his mother, they were afraid of the harmful rays of the sun. It stood to reason that they too would in time imbue him with their fear. In the sitting room they discussed truth, mythology, and relativity with the disconcerting assuredness of people who are convinced that what they are discussing did not exist. In volume one Marcel as a young boy borrowed books from a lending library. Most of the books were about aristocrats. Somewhat timidly Marcel mimicked their laughter. In the books he so avidly read all the salons of the aristocrats were rectangular in shape just like the sitting rooms of other people, except that the salons of the aristocrats were slightly larger to accommodate the pianos and the huge mirrors.

## Slides

Mrs. Dip's life has been uneventful. She has not read Proust. Seated in her small compact car, the uneventfulness of her life is a surface which she keeps traversing daily. The landmarks that stand out are all recent ones. Mrs. Dip cherishes the landmarks. Mr. Dip eating his breakfast. Mr. Dip mowing the lawn. Mr. Dip buying a five-hundred-dollar leather armchair. Mrs. Dip rewards the children by showing them slides of her living room. The slides were taken by Mr. Dip. The slides show the five-hundred-dollar armchair from every conceivable angle. There are also slides of the electric lawn mower and of the table set for breakfast. The children may be retarded, but they are quite capable of recognizing the glasses of milk and fried eggs on the table. Their reward, it turns out, is a journey through the vaguely familiar-looking world of Mr. and Mrs. Dip. Breathlessly the children wait for the breakfast shown on the slides to be consumed.

### The bed

Mr. Dip has also taken a few slides of their double king-sized bed. These slides were taken during the hopeful period of his marriage. Seeing the bed, the children begin to squirm in their retarded fashion. The bed is inviting. It is large and spotless. It is the place where Mr. and Mrs. Dip spend the night. The children are well informed. The Pueblo Indians smile tenderly as they hear the children laugh. But the slides of the bed are misleading, since on one or more than one occasion Mr. Dip has informed his wife that she smells of retarded children. Everytime she undresses he can see the children's saliva trickling down between her two firm but small breasts.

### The recklessness

Marcel Proust did not hesitate when the recklessness came pounding on his door. Despite the lateness of the hour, he permitted it to enter. There is no truth, no mythology, and only a few books of relative merit. Half groggy with sleep he dressed and left the house. Overcoming his innate shyness, he approached a man on the street and asked him where he might find the members of the upper class. You'll find most of them hunting rats in the basement of the Hotel Marigny.

Where's the hotel?

Any cabbie will take you there, said the man.

As Mr. and Mrs. Dip sat in their living room they could hear the recklessness pounding on the door of their neighbor. I don't like to hunt rats, even if one gets to meet members of the upper class in an informal setting, said Mr. Dip thoughtfully.

## The silence

Marcel may have come here because the people of Albuquerque are well known to be tolerant and exceedingly friendly to strangers. However, odds are that he came here because of the stillness. He arrived at midday and was immediately overcome by the silence. For the first two months he stayed in a small second-class hotel. Then, after visiting several real estate agencies, he bought a three-story brick building in an overwhelmingly lower-middle-class neighborhood. The previous owner of the house had been killed by the local butcher after a petty altercation. It did not really concern Marcel. He never met the man's widow. He only dealt with the real estate agent. Do you remember your childhood? the agent asked Marcel. Vividly, replied Marcel. You are lucky, said the agent. You should cherish those memories.

## The footprints

They belong to Marcel. He takes a walk early in the morning. He leaves footprints. Everyone in Albuquerque is startled by Marcel's footprints because the footprints are so small and, somehow, because they appear to be so insidious . . . their ingratiating and self-effacing outlines negating the otherwise determined stride of his walk. People are convinced that anyone capable of walking furtively yet with such a single-mindedness is clearly headed for the peak of fame.

Welcome back little Marcel, welcome back, cry Marcel's sallow-faced lower-middle-class neighbors, as he returns from his walk, invigorated, and filled with ideas for the next incident in his book.

## The first name

This is an introduction to the unreliability of the first name. In this instance the first name is Albertine. It is the name of a young woman in Marcel's eight-volume masterpiece. Day after day people keep ringing Marcel's front doorbell. Enough, he pleads, enough, I've got all the information I can use. But they insist on providing him with the latest about the retarded children, calling them the Rets. It took Marcel days to catch on. The rats, he said wonderingly, you don't say. . . They also bring him news about the cabbies and the whereabouts of the woman he loves. . . The one thing they do not bring him is the love he craves. But Marcel was waiting, and when the bell rang, he easily slipped into a faded silk dressing gown and answered the door.

My name is Albertine, said the woman. It happened to be the correct name. Marcel, as it turned out, was anticipating her arrival. There was a fire burning in his study. He stood aside to let her enter, then rushed back to his study and doused the fire. Only some notes for my book, he said in his self-deprecating way. She wasn't aware of the significance of the event at the time.

## Albertine's falsehood

I don't wish to leave you, she told Marcel. I like this quaint building, and your quaint neighbors, and all your quaint friends, and I'm dying to hear what you've written about me today.

## The longing

The cabbies in Albuquerque long for new streets and for new driving regulations. For Marcel, longing is as familiar as the quilt on his bed. He craves for the company of people who are not instantly recognized by the cabbies. Having been invited by the local RET club to participate in a panel discussion on the merits of starvation in the modern novel, Marcel refers to his hunger. I'm starved for Albertine, he declares, when it is his turn to address the twelve people in the audience, but she's never there when I want her. I have compiled a long list of her lies, infidelities, and deceptions. My longing fills me with gloom, just as I know her death will fill me with dejection. I have decided that she will be trampled to death by a horse in the fifth volume of the English edition. That much has been decided. It will give my longing a long needed respite.

## Visitors

While Marcel was amusing the members of the upper class at a fashionable resort which was only four hours by train from the center of the city, Mr. and Mrs. Dip moved into the house next door. Occasionally, while redecorating their new home, laughter from the garden next door would drift over to where they were working. Generally the laughter had an elegant ring to it. Sure enough, when Mrs. Dip peered out of the front windows she could see a large Bentley parked at the curb. Naturally, the Bentley and the uniformed chauffeur attracted a good deal of attention. People from all over came to stare quietly, without any rancor, at the old Bentley and the uniformed chauffeur. Little Marcel is having another important visitor, some said, taking pride in Marcel, taking pride in their neighborhood. No, someone else said. Marcel is away for the month. But this did not in any way diminish the pride.

## The Bentley

To this day the old bullet-proof Bentley is the favorite vehicle of the upper class. They prefer it to the Rolls because it is less ostentatious. They like the smooth ride, the leather upholstery, besides, they also save a hundred and twenty dollars on the grill. In his own inimitable manner. Marcel has tracked down all the people with a Bentley in their garage. He now feels free to call their chauffeurs by their first names. During Marcel's absence, one of his numerous society friends dropped by unannounced. Finding Albertine at home, he, out of courtesy, paid her a brief visit. It was this man's elegant laughter that drifted up to the second floor of the house next door, just as Mrs. Dip was musing over her choice of a wallpaper for the bedroom.

## Thursday (1)

Marcel had arrived in Albuquerque on a Thursday. The cabs were drawn up outside the railroad station. A solid phalanx of cabs. Only four passengers besides Marcel got off at Albuquerque. As soon as the drivers caught sight of Marcel they broke into a run. Something about his face perhaps. . . He had planned to check his luggage at the station and then enjoy a leisurely walk to the center of the city before proceeding to a hotel, but seeing the angry faces of the cabbies he instructed the porter to put his luggage quickly into the first cab. If someone had told him that the blue sky had suddenly turned the color of lead, Marcel would have believed him.

## Doubts

Marcel sees Albertine dancing with another woman at the Hotel Marigny. They are laughing. It is a coarse, disagreeable laughter. Marcel almost faints.

## The map

The map shows the large sprawling city, its squares and parks, museums and theaters, hotels and taxi stands, all within a thirty-minute drive from the large estates that surround the city. Once Marcel unfolded the map and discovered where he was located in relation to the estates, the future, it seemed to him, seemed more promising. The map also indicated the whereabouts of the small airport, and the garages where the taxi cabs are parked at night. The red circles on the map indicate where the cabbies wait for their fare. . . After nine in the evening, most of the men they pick up wish to be taken to the Albuquerque rat hunt. . . The cabbies can instantly recognize a ratter. By now all the cabbies know Marcel. He is a good tipper. They drive past his house and honk their horns, not knowing that the walls of his room have been soundproofed.

## Mr. Dip

Mr. Dip is reading because he has time on his hands. He has time on his hands because he is waiting. He wears a clean suit. Ever since his wife started to work with the retarded children, Mr. Dip has worn a freshly laundered suit each day. Mrs. Dip's salary has helped to cover the large cleaning bill, and maintain the immaculately polished interior of their house. Mr. and Mrs. Dip are not planning to have any children in the near future since they already have twelve retarded ones. Soon Mr. Dip is planning to find a companion for his five-hundred-dollar armchair.

## Names (2)

The retarded children have names. Most of the time they will acknowledge their names. Sometimes they'll pretend to have more names than one. Marcel's impromptu visit was just such an occasion. It threw everyone into a great fever, and each one of the retarded children claimed to have at least one dozen names, thereby hoping to remain at the center of Marcel's attention for the duration of his stay. Mrs. Dip introduces the children. Without being aware of it, she has introduced Marcel to the great pathos of retardation. It is not, however, an unendurable pathos for a ratter.

### Ratting

Some attempts have been made to explain ratting. The rats were pierced with hatpins or beaten with sticks. The people who attended these hunting parties soon discovered that their everyday conversations took on a new significance when certain words, such as: return, rattle, retribution, startle, tar, rather . . . were mentioned. Was Marcel aware of this when he volunteered to visit the retarded children.

### What are the retarded children thinking? (1)

They are thinking that it is soon time for supper. They are also stimulated by the slides taken by Mr. Dip. In their retarded minds they are desultorily drifting through the as yet incompletely furnished house of Mr. and Mrs. Dip. In their disturbed minds they are covering the black smooth leather of the elegant chrome armchair with the imprints of their passionate kisses. They also believe, not incorrectly, as it would appear, that Mrs. Dip is dressing to give them pleasure, that she is painting her fingernails and toenails to bring some brightness into their bleak lives. If only they knew that the saliva they drooled on Mrs. Dip's blouse was depriving Mr. Dip of his pleasure, they would in their retarded fashion most likely intensify their ardor, intensify their passionate embraces . . .

Mr. Dip gazes at the breakfast table and then looks out of the window at the New Mexico sky, thinking that another beautiful day is awaiting him at the office.

*What are the children thinking? (2)*

What are the children thinking? Their thinking can be said to be at a standstill. It is colored by the fingernails of Mrs. Dip. It is colored by her long blonde hair. The children are retarded and are learning to tie their shoelaces. Each day they are taught to use a comb. The comb has become a familiar object for their retarded minds. They have become accustomed to its presence and no longer recoil when it is put into their hands. Somehow the hair keeps growing on their retarded heads. It was hair in the first place that necessitated the invention of the comb. The comb is green with a long handle.

*The letter*

Marcel is attached to his mother. He writes from a resort hotel. He is suffering from hay fever. He has dislocated his right arm. Who is the strange man in boots who is constantly spying on poor Albertine, he wants to know. He's not a member of the upper class, that's for sure, responds his mother. Does she save my letters, wonders Marcel. So much depends on it . . . so much . . .

*Neighbors*

Marcel failed to see Mr. and Mrs. Dip move their giant bed, section by section, into the house next door. Marcel is away at a resort hotel, said his mother when Mr. Dip knocked on their door. I'm your new neighbor, explained Mr. Dip. I just wanted to borrow a cup of sugar.

*Albertine*

Marcel maintains that I conspire against him. He questions me about the man who was seen following me yesterday. In volume six he discovers my secret life. It is a lie. In volume five I am thrown by a horse. Another blatant lie. Marcel feeds on the endless lies he loves to fabricate. He feeds on my presence and then spews out the crap that his friends, the cabbies, read while waiting for their evening fares.

## Laughter

Despite the cork-lined walls, Albertine's laughter penetrates his room. Who is she embracing now? Each time she laughs he has a fleeting glimpse of her being thrown by a horse . . .

## Intimacy

Albertine reluctantly joins Marcel in his cork-lined room. She complains that it is too hot and disrobes. Carefully she lies down on his papers that are scattered all over his bed. Tell me Marcel, would you still love me if I was someone else?

You are someone else, replies Marcel. That's why I love you.

## The door

The door is attached to hinges which have been oiled. It swings open noiselessly. It permits Albertine to slip out furtively. There is no truth, there is no mythology, and there's hardly any relativity left in the world. She has by now become accustomed to the distortions in Marcel's notebooks. Still, as she intends to prove, the distortions are open to change. However, Marcel doesn't waste any time on regrets. He doesn't challenge Albertine's not entirely unforeseen departure. He simply invalidates it by chipping away at the stone steps, and in place of the entrance he has a large bay window installed, obliterating all signs of her hasty exit.

## The fencing lesson

The count's footman watches as his master gives Albertine a fencing lesson. They have to improvise a bit, because the count has sold his foils. They make do with sticks. The count is extremely watchful because there are one or two valuable vases in the room. Albertine is beside herself with excitement. Later that afternoon they go riding on the count's estate. How easily she has slipped away from Marcel. . . How skillfully she managed to open the front door after oiling the hinges. She will change her name if necessary. Marcel will never find her again.

## The cabbies

Marcel is the only one who sides with the cabbies after they have announced a wildcat strike. Marcel, for shame, says the count. The cabbies are blocking all the roads leading to the city. They are well organized. They also pose a certain threat to our safety. Their families, furthermore, have gone into the streets. Their loathsome faces are peering into our bedrooms. But nothing will change Marcel's position. In the evening his mother makes egg salad sandwiches and distributes them to the starving cabbies who are lying next to their idle machines.

## Thursday (2)

No doubt about it, Albuquerque has made a deep impression upon me, said Marcel, but it's time that I change my frame of reference. The Thursday after Albertine's departure he packed his belongings, but when he opened the front door he saw a phalanx of cabs drawn up at both ends of the street. I am a prisoner, Marcel concluded. These people need my support. They won't let me leave.

## Impatience

The silence of the city only intensifies Mrs. Dip's impatience. She can't bear to sit down with a book. She can't bear to remain inside a room for more than ten minutes. She can't bear to hear the laughter from next door knowing that she can't join in. She gets into her small car. She is protected by the windshield as the car hurtles forward. People can see her but they can't spray her with their saliva. She drives down the highway until darkness sets in. Mr. Dip is unaware that she has left the house. He is sitting on his new chair. He is sitting contentedly on his hands, humming to himself. He can't wait for it to be time to go to work again, and for the safety of the office. Yet Mr. Dip is well liked in his neighborhood. He smiles a good deal of the time. People refer to him as the cheerful young man whose wife works with retarded children. Each fresh leather armchair he acquires helps obliterate the threat of retardation. Late into the night he thinks of the perfection of furniture.

## The airport

Albertine flies over Albuquerque in a single-engine plane. It is her first solo flight. The view from the open cockpit is exhilarating. Somewhere down below Marcel is sitting in his cork-lined room writing about her. He wanted me to be thrown by a horse, but I wasn't. If only he could see her now. Sitting at his desk, engrossed by what he is writing, Marcel doesn't even hear the sound of the explosion that rips the plane apart.

# TWO POEMS

TENNESSEE WILLIAMS

## HIS MANNER OF RETURNING

It occurs at a time of stillness when you're alone and there's that
diffusion of light going into shadow slowly.
        Tall-fenced garden, tropically planted,
        the sun
dropping under palms and sea-grape trees
        between your compound
and the property of the elderly recluse, just before, homecoming,
he turns on the lamp's clouded pearl behind his kitchen shutters . . .

These being the fore-planned conditions, he is, in a way, a visitor
who is invited.
        Then? He appears, a very clear apparition.
Of what was familiar about him there remains a great deal, such as
that pride of bearing that makes him seem tall
and his moving about the place in a way that declares it his own.

Changes have taken place since he left but they seem not to
        surprise him
and you begin to feel a bit foolish, conducting him about
as you would Garden Ladies on their visiting day in the Spring.

You point out to him the spacious fish pool beneath the outside
staircase, and its witless denizens, the red mollies, the pink ones,
the ones that are opalescent.
      He seems not to care for them and, suddenly, neither do you.


Then you point out to him the new gazebo in the front rose garden,
a lacy white summer confection of a thing that might have
      been meant
for Mme. Arcadina to rustle into at dusk
      (voice clear as a bell ringing vespers)
and for her companion-playwright-lover, Trigorin,
      to look past the fading theatre of her face
at the clear youth of Nina, the sea gull that he'll shoot down,
without intention . . .

To your visitor, pointing at the gazebo, you announce:
"This is the Jane Bowles summerhouse."
And you go on compounding sentiment with sentiment, saying
"It's octagonal, you see, eight-sided like all questions are
that many-sided, at least. And on each of its eight sides there
is a brass plate engraved with the name of someone whom I've loved.
Here's yours, you see, between the rose vines that are beginning
to climb."


      Then his detachment gives place
to that old withering way of putting down the Bavarian burgher
      in you.
You hear his whispering dryly:
      "Loved? You?"


And so you fall silent beside him, an outcry rising in you but held
between throat and tongue, one tasteless indiscretion, this cry
that you will not commit.

      *Then?*
Something sounds or moves, to the right or left,
and you turn, startled, that way for only a moment.
But the moment's enough, for he only needed that moment
      of inattention
to his presence for him to elude again,

those vulgarities of the living which aren't and never were his
but which you have tried once more to impose on his apparition
as if you didn't know that apparitions require a delicacy of approach
which isn't your style at all.

Well, now that it's finished, the ceremonial visit,
don't you feel somehow relieved? With the light and shadow
resuming the usual and comfortable order of their retreat
        into nightfall?

All nearly all dark now except for the kitchen lamp of the recluse,
back of his kitchen shutters, open a little,
and gently, now, his noiseless hand extended to draw them shut?

A gesture of conclusion that's necessary . . .


## NIGHT VISIT

It was winter and late at night, an hour or two before the first
gray concession to morning.

                    For several weeks
I had been living alone, not answering the telephone which had
now grown tired of ringing.
        I had no plans, and was almost comforted somewhat
        by the absence of any.
(What are the plans of a stupefied being?)

On the very few occasions when I had compelled myself to go out
I had been tortured by an inability to speak much more than
        an apology
for not speaking.
        In such a condition it is possible to be intolerably lonely
whether you know it or not.

            There was, in the downstairs hall of the highrise
                apartment building

an electric device that permitted you, if you wished,
to communicate with someone calling you from the guarded
    entrance.
    That late night
it sounded repeatedly and with the irregularity of a failing
    heartbeat.
And I, who had not slept but was stupefied to the point of
    scarcely knowing what I was doing if I did anything,
staggered out of bed at last to answer the call.

"Who is it?"
"Helen."
(A girl who had abruptly disappeared from my life and the lives
of everyone I knew who had known her—completely as if she had
never existed.)
"Helen?"
"Yes, Helen."
"Helen, I'm pushing the buzzer. Come on up to Apartment C
on the twenty-eighth floor."

I met an apparition, and so did she.
She was lovely as ever and even more fragile than ever and
    her eyes
were blind-looking.
    I found myself able to think and speak a little.
    "What have you been doing lately, Helen?"
    Indifferently she said: "When you take pills around
        the clock
what you do is try to get money to pay the drugstore."

Neither of us seemed to care, or to be aware,
that there were such unnatural stretches of silence between
these few things we said.

"Do you know, you must know, about the death of
    my friend?"
"Yes, I know, and I wished that it had been you. Will you
give me cab fare to Olympic, New Jersey?"
    I said that I would.
"What pills have you got here?"

I looked more closely at her blind-looking eyes and said that I
could give her a couple of Milltowns.

"Big deal. Forget it."

It was like being in a room with a moth that could talk.
"Helen, you've gotten too thin."
"Yes, well, I suppose so. Someone I didn't know
came up to me in a bar and said, 'Young lady, you're
killing yourself.'"
It was honestly and indifferently reported . . .

A visit late at night, quiet voices, and good-bys that would
doubtless be final.

# CORRIDORS

An excerpt from the novel *The Life of Jesus*

TOBY OLSON

AUTHOR'S NOTE ON The Life of Jesus: *To a boy raised in the bosom of the Catholic Church in the early 40s, the life of Jesus and the Holy Family was felt as his own idealized autobiography. His mother was of course a Virgin. His father, who was ill and died young, was more a watcher than a participant. And he himself was guilty, because he was not Jesus and could not cure his father. "Corridors" is a result of that somewhat tortured matrix. (It is only after this section of the novel that Jesus is able to proceed to his own necessary death, to return to His father.)*

*The mythology of this novel is constructed from that sense of The Life of Jesus which was received by a young boy, in Catholic school, from the Bible stories of Irish nuns.*

He remembers he came to the town in a boat. In the late summer; in the afternoon; a bright sky, and he could see buildings a mile off, of various shapes, the sun hitting them. They seemed to come clear to the water's edge, had been built the moment the people had landed, as permanent shelter. But they were big, and as they came closer, he saw in their shadow the place where the wharf had been built: in front of the buildings, a place where the boat could dock. If it were to dock, but in this case it wasn't. It would pull up straight to the pier, turn at the last moment, sidle along the old boards, and he would have to jump (possibly two feet) over gunnels and onto the landed wood.

They'd talked about this. His mother had said: "The boat will pull up straight to the pier; it will turn at the last moment, sidle along the old rubber tires, and you will have to jump, about two feet, over the gunnels and onto the wood of the dock." "Won't my legs push the boat back when I push off?" "No, the boat is too big to be moved like that; just jump when I tell you; you'll be all right."

That he had not come to the town by land was somehow important, marvelous still, to him after seven years. He'd go in a rowboat, sometimes, out to a safe distance, and then he would head in quick and try to reclaim the feeling. But rowing, he'd have to look over his shoulder, and he couldn't go as smooth or fast enough, and it was never the same. Besides, he had begun to see the town from over a mile out to sea, and it wasn't safe to row out that far.

He was six years old; the center of his experience of the town was now at a point a half mile of water away from it. And the wharf had begun to form; people were sitting on chests on the dock; someone was moving and selling something; to the right was a fisherman, casting his net; the dots of old tires, a few gulls sitting on pilings, swirls of oil in the water. "What if the boat's wash pushes it back out for a minute, just when I'm jumping?" "I'll watch for that; I'll tell you when." "Will somebody catch me if I start to fall back?" "Yes; don't worry about it now."

He had always thought it as strange, that he knew the town best from a different element, a literal place over water, from the prow of a boat. It would have been one thing to come to the town over land, following road signs, riding or walking. Even if he had been alone, and not with his mother, he would have come to it gradually, it would not have seemed such a solid place. The way one walks from the straight, planned areas of the suburbs, into the twisted streets of the city: the change is so gradual; the city only slowly gathers around you; but even if it were not for that, the ground is the same ground. But to come to it over water: the city has almost a line that defines it: the wharf, the outermost pilings, the immediate sea.

But earlier on, in the ship's hold, sitting beside his mother (her arm round his shoulder); nobody else, but the seamen coming below, at various times, to check them; some being gentle and kind. But you could never tell when the light got cut off, that shaft down the passage, a corridor, through which came some man, maybe the one with the leer, maybe the one who brought water; head in his mother's armpit: "How far are we now?" "Only a little while, a little while yet."

1

The City is a real city: the people live in the streets or in houses, lining the streets, facing away from them. The streets are running with garbage, with animal offal, the side streets running with human excrement. No gutters, but corridors carved by the rain pushing through cabbages and shit, to someplace indistinguishable. The City could be said to rage and seethe or, it is foolish to speak of the City as raging and seething, for the City is not human: is not people, garbage or houses.

He comes to himself on a street in the heart of the City. He is unsettled by his own presence there, as if he has come to meet an important person. He tells his apostles to leave him, and then he takes up a post where the street turns into a small square at the center of the City, and the people begin to approach him.

First are the women with young children: limbs that he touches with both hands, the mothers kissing the hem of his robes. And then come the blind and the lepers, and one man who cannot speak, and Jesus touches his tongue with his own spittle, and the man leaves him uttering nouns. A man comes up to him and says: "This is what I did in life," and he begins to dance and tumble, sometimes walking on his hands, sinking into the muck of the street up to his wrists. And spins on his toes, dragging his left leg, like a thin stick, but grotesquely swollen and arthritic at the knee, which suppurates like a rotten cabbage. And Jesus touches the knee and cures it, and the man walks away firmly, no longer playing the acrobat, in a stately posture. And the rest come, each in their place and order.

And then after a few hours of curing, he begins to reckon some similar faces returning. "Why do you come back again?" And the man who had danced says: "The pain has moved from my leg to my stomach, and I have to walk bent over." And Jesus touches the man's stomach and cures him. And others come back (a man who'd been blind now feigning dumbness, motions to Jesus to touch his tongue with his spittle, and shudders when the Master does so). And the lepers return with headaches, and Jesus can hear people, going away, talking of the relative pleasures of the various cures: "When he touched my tongue with spit, I could barely stand it!" And then he begins in earnest. He is curing a man who has returned to him six times, and each time with a different ailment, a different location and intensity of pain. He had come first as a leper, dragging a pus-filled leg, and Jesus had touched his leg and cured him. Then he had returned in an hour, a deep pain in the middle of his chest. The third time his eyes bulged, seemed ready to jump from his face, and Jesus had touched his eyes with spittle, and they had receded. And now the man is standing before him. He has lost considerable weight, he complains of a pain in the head, and Jesus walks carefully around him, touching the various parts of his body; he measures his limbs with a bit of string; he measures the circumference of his head, and then he stands facing the man; and then he strikes him full in the face. The man rocks back on his heels; the pain sinks through his chest to his stomach; he becomes incontinent; the pain escapes from his body in feces and urine and runs in its own rivulet, into a corridor in the street.

2

It is at least possible that the ship will not get close to the wharf. Two feet is very close; it's a big ship. Even four feet is close, and I doubt that I could jump that far. But if my mother stood behind me and gave me a good push, the arc of my jump might take me that distance, at least get one foot on the edge of the dock, and someone would surely grab me. If my father were here, he would build a board, like a gangplank, about twenty feet long (the width of the ship). I'd help him attach it to one side of the ship with hinges. We'd use heavy wooden pegs to secure it. While we sailed it would rest across the gunnels. And then, after the ship had turned, in order to sidle up along the wharf, we'd flop the board over, so that it would hit the dock, and I'd jump up and run down it, onto the safety of the wharf.

3

Why do you stand in the street? Why do you allow them six visits? What is the nature of the message? Is the City a human being? Why do you cure them singly? Why must you touch their bodies?

Why do you distinguish women? How could you send us away?
How did we get to this City?

A house is offered, and Jesus takes them into it and through it
to a bath at the rear; the bath provides the livelihood of the owner
of the house, but he gives it over to Jesus, who has cured his son,
for nothing. The bath is narrow, and along one side of the room is
a long bench, and Jesus tells his apostles to remove their shoes and
be seated on the bench.

They sit in a row in their robes; some cross their legs; others sit
with both feet, together, on the floor. Their sandals have provided
little protection and their feet are covered with offal and various
dirts. Jesus can tell, by reading their feet, where they have been.

He takes up the first foot in the line and begins to wash it. He
uses a cloth and a small brush. Someone has provided a basin of
warm soapy water, and he moistens his cloth, occasionally. He
washes with exactitude, but quickly, but as he proceeds he slows
down, lingering over each foot for a long time, washing each foot
in a way particular to its anatomy, shape and structure. Peter is last
in the line, and when he reaches Peter's feet, Jesus takes time to
consider. He does not touch Peter's feet right away, but directs
Peter to lift each foot and turn it, so that he might better look at
it. And then he takes up the left foot of Peter. And Peter feels the
Master's hand like some incredible fine shoe, one he knows he
could walk on forever; the Master's palm forms to his arch; his
index finger divides his large toe from the second, but feels like a
strap of velvet formed to the space between them. Then Jesus
proceeds to wash Peter's feet. He produces a small brush from his
garments and carefully scrubs at the cuticle of each nail. Where
there are spots of cracked dirt between the toes, the Master bends
and moistens the place with his tongue, so the dirt softens and
runs to the floor. Peter squirms on the bench, constantly moving
his head in order always to see the Master's hands, his face, his
pink tongue, washing the dirt away. "This is Jesus," he repeats to
himself; "he is putting his lips on my feet; my feet are the farthest
point of my body; it is like he is kissing my face." And then Jesus
rubs at the calluses with a piece of mortar, goes over the heel, the
ball of each foot, the tips of the toes; he pares down the nails with
a small, sharp knife; he takes each toe into his mouth, and swirls
his tongue around it. And as Jesus moves his tongue down and
between each toe, Peter can feel, in his own mouth, as if his teeth
were the toes, and the Master's tongue is moving across his gums,

slowly, identifying each tooth separately, curing the roots, moving on. And Peter feels that his teeth are breaking into words, that from now on each tooth will have a separate and distinct movement when he speaks, so that his words will have a new, incredibly complex generative power of inflection, that he will never say the same thing twice again. And even then, as the Master holds his small toe in his mouth, their eyes locked together, Peter can feel the first real sound of his life. It rises up from his stomach, passes his larynx, takes particular shape in his mouth and enters the room as a moan. And each object in the room changes; the room becomes —literally—a new place. And when Peter looks back at the face of the Savior, he sees he is smiling, his bared teeth sunk into his toe; a trickle of blood is running down his exquisite chin.

4

He remembers carrying his father on his back, walking down steps, and placing his father in automobiles. Sometimes he'd only be taking his father out of the house for air. His father never liked to sit in a chair in the yard, but wanted to sit right down on the grass itself; and so, at these times, he would have to walk to the edge of the house, allowing his father to hold to the side of the building, to slide from his back and rest in an awkward way in the grass.

His father was not heavy, was easy to hold, and yet he was always afraid to carry him. If he had thought of his father as a permanent cripple, if they had at least spoken of him in that way, he might have mastered the act, been able to carry his father in comfort. His father would turn in his chair, away from the table, and he would face away from his father, bend at the knees and await his father's hand on his shoulder. He knew his father was grimacing behind him, working to lift himself, a little off the chair, using his crutches, both in one hand, to aid him. Then he would feel his father's hand on his shoulder, would reach round behind him, grasping his father's bony buttocks. His father would release the crutches; someone would take them, and then he would wrap the bone of his forearm under the chin and across the neck of his son, and the son would raise up slowly, letting his hands slip from his father's hips down to the back of his knees, and would stand up, the light weight of his father upon his back. The left knee of his father was swollen the size of a cabbage; the lower leg on that

side hung like a piece of thin tin along the thigh of the son. He'd
hold the crook of the right leg in his wrist; he'd hold the left knee
like a cabbage resting in the palm of his hand. His father usually
rested too low on the son's back, but he dared not hitch him up,
for this was an awkward position for his father, and any movement
would cause him pain. He always feared he would fall, and would
literally, break his father in two, or would fall on top of his father,
crushing the almost empty cup of his hips; would crush his delicate
ribs with his own spine, falling upon him. He imagined how it
would be, to leap up from the bed of his father's body, turn round
and see his father's face as he cursed him through the pain of his
last breaths. Once, while carrying his father, he misjudged the
width of a doorway, had banged his father's left knee into the side
of it. His father had cried out in pain, cursed him and began beating him feebly on the head and shoulders. He'd been so surprised
he'd dropped his father's right leg, and felt his father begin to slip.
But his father had grabbed tight to his throat with his left arm, had
kept cursing and striking him, saying "Go on! Jesus Christ! Go on!"
and he had gone on, weaving from side to side, down the stone
steps, had turned, backing his father into the seat of the car.

Sometimes his father would become incontinent at the table.
He always watched his father try to eat, and could tell, at such
times, as his father's face would begin to sweat, his teeth to grind
together; his eyes would widen, with trying to control his sphincter,
losing the battle: the sound of the gas, the shuddering of his
father's body, the gurgling sound of the shit leaving. When only
the family was present his father could withstand it, would say
things like "Here it comes again," would manage a feeble smile.
But when guests were present, his father could not hold back his
humiliation; his head would drop to his chest, and he and his
mother would carry the chair with his father rocking in it, away
from the table and into the nearest bathroom; and he would leave
them, giving his father over, to the secret care of his mother.

He remembers they carried his father into a room. They were
good friends of his father's, old school chums, and his father had
lost some bet or other, to them, and they had picked him up, laughing and joking, as when people are picked up before they are
thrown into a lake, and had carried him into a room in the house,
had closed the door after them. When they carried his father in he
was large and robust.

He did not see his father again for a long time. But he slept in the room next to his father's room, and he could hear things, if only vaguely, through the walls. Often his mother would go into his father's room, and he would hear the sounds of the bed squeaking, limbs striking against the wall. Neither had his father's chums come out of the room, but one of them would occasionally call to him from the door and send him to get things from the store: a rope, a hammer, pieces of wire, two metal rings, and occasionally baby food.

And then he himself fell sick, with a fungus infection that completely covered both of his feet. He lay in the adjoining room, both feet out of the covers extended over the edge of the bed. They had put towels on the floor under his feet, and the towels became gradually matted with pus and scabs. The feet themselves were like two rotting indistinguishable vegetables, that seemed to shudder and breathe with a life of their own. He could not sleep, fell into delirium, was in constant pain. And then in the middle of the night he saw his father standing in the doorway. He was not sure how he knew it was his father, for the figure his father had been was now bent and emaciated. He was naked, and the son could see there were various devices attached to his father's body. Both of his father's wrists had been pierced with hooks; his left knee had a thin electrical wire running from it, with a plug affixed to the end. His father still wore his belt, but the belt was now so large that it could have encompassed two fathers, and his father had to hold onto the belt in order to keep it from falling into a large circle at his feet. "My son," the father said; and the son leapt out of his bed, staggering on his ruined feet, but before he could reach his father someone jerked his father back into the other room, and before the son fell to the floor he glimpsed, through the closing door, an incredible device like an upright rack, affixed to the wall of the room.

5

Now I remember a time before the beginning of the journey. I am still sitting with my head tucked in my mother's armpit; we are still on the boat; but I remember a time in the Midwest, in which I have broken my clavicle. My father sits in a white summer suit on the porch of our house. They are tearing a side of the building away, to put in a picture window, facing a crab-apple tree. My room faces the top branches of the tree. But I am sitting on the porch with my father. A violent electric storm is beginning. And there are old photographs and movies, in which I am standing or moving, in the park across from the house, under the corridor the trees make, beside a plaque of the names of the war dead; or I am running, in a soldier suit, with a model airplane in my hands, across the lawn of the park, to where my father sits waiting in the grass. And then I am walking the four long blocks from school (with my broken clavicle). I begin to mimic the new limp of my father. And as I am moving along, Lady comes out of the hedge two hundred yards away; she turns, and faces me. The sidewalk is narrow, lined all the way along with hedges on both sides. Even at this distance she is larger than I am, and there is no escape. She is running, and what I remember are the last few feet of her run: the way I am guarding my arm with my books, the fixed shape of the dog in the air, the slow arc of her trajectory.

I don't know who's running this ship; I imagine my father somewhere in the workings of it. It moves now in a straight line, as if through a trough in the water. The distance is shrinking, the dock beginning to form itself. I see the figures of animals and humans. Let it be two feet away. Let it hold for a moment.

6

He is twelve years old. He is dressed only in underwear. His mother is carrying him on her back. They pass over the threshold and out of the room. Someone quickly closes the door behind them. His feet dangle like rotting vegetables. His mother speaks to the crowd which has gathered: "Look, I have given birth to a son!"

7

If they had come to the gates of the City, before the shipwreck, still in the faint guiding light of the late afternoon. If Jesus had not washed their feet. If the streets of the City did not run with vegetables and excrement. If it were not called Babylon. If the people lived in the City and did their work and when they got sick, were cured, and remained so. If no man offered his house. If the streets of the City were not narrow corridors, but straight and as wide as twelve men in a row. If Peter had not demanded to be carried; if he had understood the parable. If they had not lost their way and come at last to the dock.

8

And so he had become his father's child, though born out of strange circumstance. Finally, they had brought his father out of the room, had placed him in a wheelchair at the kitchen table. The wheelchair would not fit through any opening in the house; it was not collapsible, and yet surely they had not built the wheelchair inside the house or built the house around it, but at times he saw the wheelchair outside, in the grass, his father resting comfortably in it. At night or in the afternoon, when they had placed his father in bed, he would push the wheelchair around the house, looking for exits. He would bang it against doorways, try lifting it through windows, but it would not break or collapse.

And then he began to fall sick often. And during such times, he would beg his mother to bring the wheelchair into his room, saying vaguely, "It gives me a certain comfort." And he would lie awake with his ear crusted with scabs over suppurating wounds or his feet throbbing with draining advanced fungus, and would look at the wheelchair, would sometimes reach out and touch it from his bed, would get up and rub himself against its firm metal. And sometimes, late in the night, he would think that his father was under the bed that he slept in; he would fancy his father was thinking of him, would imagine his father reaching out, his arm moving across the floor: his hand closes around a spoke; he pulls the wheelchair closer to the son's bed.

But the son remembers a day when they had taken his father and placed him in the grass beside a large walnut tree in the front yard. They were talking, but his father was not listening, was looking up into the higher branches of the tree. And then his father took a pencil from his pocket and a scrap of paper, and placing the paper on his knee, he wrote, upside down and backwards, so that the son could read it directly as it was written: *let's get some nuts.* And then he began carefully to help his father, who constantly cursed him, "Christ, be careful!" until his father was standing, holding onto the thick trunk of the tree. And after he had helped to lift his father into the lower limbs, he stood back, beside his mother, who had come out of the house and was wringing her hands. And his father slowly made his way into the higher branches, cursing and moaning, shaking the tree as he moved. And the nuts began to fall to the ground, and among them the son could see occasional pieces of fingernail, small bits of skin, drops of blood, spirochetes of hair. And when his father had reached the highest limb, which was the richest of all, he gave it a violent shake, and a hundred nuts were thrust down their shafts to the ground. And then his father rested, suspended in the branches, like a spider, his body came to stasis. And looking through the leaves and branches the son found his father's face, and his father smiled, and the stigmata passed into the son's palms.

9

A quarter mile out, and now he can see how the people take shape into occupations. There are people simply sitting and waiting. The fisherman hauls in his net. A man sells nuts, baking on a steaming cart. He holds close to his mother's body; they are standing in the prow of the ship. And down from a road that ends at the dock itself, he sees a group of men, who proceed carefully; they are intent on watching where they put their feet. One of them is carried, by two men, who hold him as if he were seated in a moving chair. His feet are brilliantly white, and they hang and sway at the end of his legs like large delicate honeydew melons.

"Two feet," he thinks, and turns his face to his mother's, for the ship is now coming to the dock, is beginning to turn, in order to sidle along the old boards and tires, and he will have to jump, possibly two feet, over the gunnels and onto the wood of the dock. "Will they catch me if . . ." and his mother assures him they'll catch him.

The ship turns slowly; the approach is accurate; the thirteen men seem bewildered at finding themselves on the wharf. He stands, with his mother's help, on the gunnels. The stern of the ship overshoots the arc of the intended turn; it crashes into the corner of the dock; a large hole is ripped in its underbelly; water rushes into the voids. One of the thirteen men extends his hands, and beckons to the boy. The boy squats on the gunnels; his mother grasps him by the buttocks; he thrusts himself into the air. The stern of the ship overshoots the arc of the intended turn; the prow overcorrects; it crashes into the side of the dock; the dock begins to buckle; water rushes into the forward voids. The boy slips on the gunnels, falls back on his mother; he crushes her body beneath him; water rushes over the deck; the chalice of her hips is splayed and broken; she curses at the son as she drifts away. The ship comes in at a perfect angle, sidles along the old tires lining the wharf; the boy squats on the gunnels; his mother holds onto his buttocks; everyone rushes to the side of the ship to wave good-by; the weight throws the ship out of balance; it begins to list; the boy leaps into the air; the superstructure crashes around him, splitting the dock into pieces. The boy rushes across the breaking dock; he reaches the mouth of the street; the twelve men gather around him; the thirteenth man is missing. The ship rocks away from the dock; the returning wave of its wash speeds it back out to sea. His mother stands in the stern of the ship; she holds her veil round her face at the neck; she waves back at him with her handkerchief.


10


And now have I come to the Fabulous City. I float over it. A mile from shore, in a boat, a twelve-foot skiff, that does not rest at anchor; the sea is so calm and flat. I float in a circle, my prow raised by the weight of myself in the stern; turn, past the sea and the other city at a distance, empty. No clouds. No real sun. The blue dome; the inside of a blue egg. The flat sea. The slow turn of the boat.

And under me, the City rests in the care of the water, through which I can see, as if through a clarity of crystal. Fish, and long vines and sea grass, at the edge of the circle, in which my boat floats, turns on the viscous surface; slightly convex, my boat like a dark pupil, in the center of a still blue eye.

Float. Turn. And below me, the superstructure, the barnacled gunnels of the huge ship, as large as a city, changed in a new element: starfish, sand dollars in rows, around it on the sandy bottom. The whole thing seems to list; the board cross the gunnels rises at its loose end, in the currents, and falls back, with no sound.

Sinews of loose beams and guy wires, tendons and ligaments of cable and rope, I know now, which are the parts of my father's body, that have not been rotted or wasted, but wrested, from the possible hands of morticians, into usefulness, into specific potency.

And the caulking a mixture of clarified body fat and diseased tissues. And the braided cables are his tendons. The ropes are oiled and protected from rot with synovia and mucus. And the chinks in the injured voids have been cured with his tissues. And over the deck of the wheel house, his stretched skin. And under the glass dome of the compass, his brain.

My boat turns, and turns quicker. At the edge of my circle: the beginning of a whirlpool, turning slightly; my boat is beginning to descend. And the sky becomes electric. And storm covers the city; a black cloud, I can see, as my boat turns, obliterates the city. Torsion of the boat turning, now quickly. Nothing but water around me.

And now I can see as my boat lowers; I look over its side, down in the clear water; my boat slows in its motion; it hovers at a level with the highest mast, turning ever so slightly, above the ship. A wheelchair waits on the deck below me, a blanket, folded, over its metal arm. And then the door of the wheel house opens; my mother comes out of it; she carefully descends the ladder, carrying a chalice in her free hand.

And now the City rises to meet me. The boat stops turning, descends, past superstructure and wires, then comes to rest on the deck.

And my mother comes up to greet me then; she hands me my crutches, on which I raise myself, and helps me to sit down in my chair, and aids me in folding the blanket across my knees. And then she hands me my chalice and kisses my cheek.

And then my mother looks up at the wheel house for a moment; she nods, and then she turns back to me. "Hold tight," she says. And with a slight gentle jerk, the ship rocks free of the bottom and rises; and soon our prow breaks the surface; the ship emerges; the water spills, down its washed sides and rushes over our ankles. And for a while the ship rests and bobs on the flat surface. And while the sun is drying our clothing and hair, we talk of our lives together. We are tender. We laugh often.

And then my mother looks up at the wheel house again, and then she turns and looks back at me. "It's time to go," she says, and reaches and locks the wheels of my chair in place, and then she holds tight to the chair's back.

And I am sitting in my chair in the broad prow of the ship; my mother stands behind me, one hand touching my shoulder. We look out from the prow, into the flat empty surface of the sea. And then the ship plots out its course. His brain rotates under the glass dome of the compass. And the City, moves away, from shipwreck.

# SIX POEMS FROM
# *LOS ESPACIOS AZULES*

HOMERO ARIDJIS

*Translated by Brian Swann*

1

To the secret names
water carries
to the names
air touches in light
to the names
fire lifts in the flame
to the names
earth opens in flowers
to the white living universe
that sleeps beneath my body
to all of man
to Him
to the secret names

2

Faster than thought the image moves
rising in a spiral round     within your body
like sap or tunic or ivy of sounds

Faster than sight your image moves
laying hours aside and abandoning echoes
nests and words of creation swaying

Faster than the image the image moves
that seeks you in light's chasm that is shadow
and finds you visible in the invisible
like someone that living shines

Behind time and before the image moves
Inside the image another image moves
Faster than speed thought moves


3

Angels feel themselves in light

they shine invisible between
the seeing and the seen

they leave in the sky
a very clear trace

and in the trees
an open fruit

in eyes they beget
a dreamlike being

and in the heart a joy
resembling themselves


4

Clear and visible
cradling its beams in the water

the hour wavers
within dawns of coldness

among the gaps of darkness
it seems hollow in its whiteness

and in its young orient glow
pistils and sap of worn purple

a tree signals like a green pendulum
the birth of yellows in its face

and encloses the flame for a moment
with green sound

the hour
is complete over the crystal of dawn

it moves neither light nor colors
but turns the world


5

Summer in the heat is a nest
a kingdom that burns sleepily
animalia green and alive

beasts sanctified by sun's rigor
are mobile with dreams and organism
the air's plants with leaves
rocking an insect on their pinnacles

branches that lift and bend trembling
basking above the shade above the river
thickets sky pierces
open here an eye there a flower

In deeper root and higher ear
an intense clamor
an eager growth
overflows like a thanksgiving

each creature each shadow each echo
lifts toward beginning day
a quivering song of thin hymns

6

The song under the mist
lights a road
in its drift

dawn
opens in a bird's nest
light

the sun
catches the poem
already alive

the fruit
watched
becomes heavy

it moves its shadow
in the tree

# LILY'S PARTY

JAMES PURDY

As Hobart came through the door of Crawford's Home Dinette, his eyes fell direct on Lily sitting alone at one of the big back tables, eating a piece of pie.

"Lily! Don't tell me! You're supposed to be in Chicago!" he ejaculated.

"Who supposed I was to be?" Lily retorted, letting her fork cut quickly into the pie.

"Well, I'll damn me if—" he began to speak in a humming sort of way while pulling out a chair from under her table, and sitting down unbidden. "Why, everybody thought you went up there to be with Edward."

"Edward! He's the last person on this earth I would go anywhere to be with. And I think you know that!" Lily never showed anger openly, and if she was angry now at least she didn't let it stop her from enjoying her pie.

"Well, Lily, we just naturally figured you had gone to Chicago when you weren't around."

"I gave your brother Edward two of the best years of my life," Lily spoke with the dry accent of someone testifying in court for a second time. "And I'm not about to go find him for more of what he gave me. Maybe you don't remember what I got from him, but I do . . ."

"But where were you, Lily . . . We all missed you!" Hobart harped on her absence.

99

"I was right here all the time, Hobart, for your information." As she said this, she studied his mouth somewhat absent-mindedly. "But as to your brother, Edward Starr," she continued, and then paused as she kept studying his mouth as if she found a particular defect there which had somehow escaped scrutiny hitherto. "As to Edward," she began again, and then stopped, struck her fork gingerly against the plate, "he was a number-one poor excuse for a husband, let me tell you. He left me for another woman, if you care to recall, and it was because of his neglect that my little boy passed away. . . So let's say I don't look back on Edward, and am not going to any Chicago to freshen up on my recollections of him. . ."

She quit studying his mouth, and looked out the large front window through which the full October moon was beginning its evening climb.

"At first I will admit I was lonesome and with my little boy lying out there in the cemetery, I even missed as poor an excuse for a man as Edward Starr, but believe you me, that soon passed."

She put down her fork now that she had eaten all the pie, laid down some change on the bare white ash wood of the table, and then closing her purse, sighed, and softly rose.

"I only know," Lily began, working the clasp on her purse, "that I have begun to find peace now. . . Reverend McGilead, as you may be aware, has helped me toward the light. . ."

"I have heard of Reverend McGilead," Hobart said in a voice so sharp she looked up at him while he held the screen door open for her.

"I am sure you have heard nothing but good then," she shot back in a voice that was now if not deeply angry, certainly unsteady.

"I will accompany you home, Lily."

"You'll do no such thing, Hobart. . . Thank you, and good evening."

He noticed that she was wearing no lipstick, and that she did not have on her wedding ring. She also looked younger than when she had been Edward Starr's wife.

"You say you have found peace with this new preacher," Hobart spoke after her retreating figure. "But under this peace, you hate Edward Starr," he persisted. "All you said to me tonight was fraught with hate."

She turned briefly and looked at him, this time in the eyes. "I will find my way, you can rest assured, despite your brother and you."

He stayed in front of the door of the dinette, and watched her walk down the moonlit-white road toward her house that lay in deep woods. His heart beat violently. All about where he stood were fields and crops and high trees, and the sailing queen of heaven was the only real illumination after one went beyond the dinette. No one came down this small road with the exception of lovers who occasionally used it for their lane.

Well, Lily is a sort of mystery woman, he had to admit to himself. And where, then, did the rumor arise that she had been to Chicago. And now he felt she had lied to him, that she had been in Chicago after all and had just got back.

Then without planning to do so, hardly knowing indeed he was doing so, he began following after her from a conveniently long distance down the moonlit road. After a few minutes of pursuing her, he saw someone come out from one of the ploughed fields. The newcomer was a tall still youthful man with the carriage of an athlete rather than that of a farmer. He almost ran toward Lily. Then they both stopped for a moment, and after he had touched her gently on the shoulder they went on together. Hobart's heart beat furiously, his temple throbbed, a kind of film formed over his lips from his mouth rushing with fresh saliva. Instead of following them directly down the road, he now edged into the fields and pursued them more obliquely. Sometimes the two ahead of him would pause, and there was some indication the stranger was about to leave Lily, but then from something they said to one another, the couple continued on together. Hobart would have liked to get closer to them so that he might hear what they were saying, but he feared discovery. At any rate, he could be sure of one thing, the man walking with her was not Edward, and also he was sure that whoever he was he was her lover. Only lovers walked that way together, too far apart at one time, too weaving and close together another time: their very breathing appeared uneven and heavy the way their bodies swayed. Yes, Hobart realized, he was about to see love being made, and it made him walk unsteadily, almost to stumble. He only hoped he could keep a rein on his feelings and would not make his presence known to them.

When he saw them at last turn into her cottage he longed for the strength to leave them, to go back home to forget Lily, forget his brother Edward, whom he was certain Lily had been "cheat-ing" all through their marriage (even *he* had been intimate once with Lily when Edward was away on a trip, so that he had always wondered if the child she bore him in this marriage might not have been after all his, but since it was dead, he would not think of it again).

Her cottage had a certain fame. There were no other houses about, and the windows of her living room faced the thick forest. Here she could have done nearly whatever she liked and nobody would have been the wiser, for unless one had stood directly before the great window which covered almost the entire width of her room, any glimpse within was shut out by foliage, and sometimes by heavy mist.

Hobart knew that this man, whoever he was, had not come to-night for the purpose of imparting Jesus' love to her but his own. He had heard things about the young preacher, Reverend Mc-Gilead, he had been briefed on his "special" prayer meetings, and had got the implication the man of the cloth had an excess of unburned energy in his make-up. He shouted too loud during his sermons, people said, and the veins in his neck were ready to burst with the excess of blood that ran through him.

From Hobart's point of observation, in the protection of a large spruce tree, nothing to his surprise he saw whom he believed to be the young preacher take her in his arms. But then what hap-pened was unforeseen, undreamed of indeed, for with the rapidity of a professional gymnast, the preacher stripped off his clothing in a trice, and stood in the clear illumination of her room not covered by so much as a stitch or thread. Lily herself looked paralyzed, as rodents are at the sudden appearance of a serpent. Her eyes were unfocused on anything about her, and she made no attempt to assist him as he partially undressed her. But from the casual way he acted, it was clear they had done this before. Yes, Hobart con-fessed to himself, in the protective dark of the tree under which he stood, one would have expected certainly something more grad-ual from lovers. He would have thought that the young preacher would have talked to her for at least a quarter of an hour, that he would have finally taken her hand, then perhaps kissed her, and then oh so slowly and excitingly, for Hobart at least, would have undressed her, and taken her to himself.

But this gymnast's performance quite nonplused the observer by the spruce tree. For one thing the gross size of the preacher's sex, its bulging veins and unusual angry redness reminded him of sights seen by him when he had worked on a farm. It also recalled a surgical operation he had witnessed performed by necessity in a doctor's small overcrowded office. The preacher now had pushed Lily against the wall, and worked vigorously at, and then through her. His eyes rolled like those of a man being drawn unwillingly into some kind of suction machine, and saliva suddenly poured out of his mouth in great copiousness so that he resembled someone blowing up an enormous balloon. His neck and throat were twisted convulsively, and his nipples tightened as if they were being given over to rank torture.

At this moment, Hobart, without realizing he was doing so, came out from his hiding place, and strode up to the window, where he began waving his arms back and forth in the manner of a man flagging a truck. (Indeed Lily later was to believe that she thought she had seen a man with two white flags in his hands signaling for help.)

Lily's screams at being discovered broke the peace of the neighborhood, and many watchdogs from about the immediate vicinity began barking in roused alarm.

"We are watched!" she was finally able to get out. Then she gave out three uncadenced weak cries. But the preacher, his back to the window, like a man in the throes of some grave physical malady, could only concentrate on what his body dictated to him, and though Lily now struggled to be free of him, this only secured him the more tightly to her. Her cries now rose in volume until they reached the same pitch as that of the watchdogs.

Even Hobart, who had become as disoriented perhaps as the couple exhibited before him, began making soft outcries, and he continued to wave his arms fruitlessly.

"No, no, and no!" Lily managed now to form and speak these words. "Whoever you are out there, go, go away at once!"

Hobart now came directly up to the window. He had quit waving his arms, and he pressed his nose and mouth against the pane.

"It's me," he cried reassuringly. "Hobart, Edward Starr's brother! Can't you see?" He was, he managed to realize, confused as to what he now should do or say, but he thought that since he had frightened them so badly and so seriously disturbed their pleasure, he had best identify himself, and let them know he meant no harm. But his calling to them only terrified Lily the more, and caused her young partner to behave like someone struggling in deep water.

"Hobart Starr here!" the onlooker called to them, thinking they may have mistook him for a housebreaker.

"Oh merciful Lord," Lily moaned. "If it is you Hobart Starr, please go away. Have that much decency—" she tried to finish the sentence through her heavy breathing.

The preacher at this moment tore off the upper part of Lily's dress, and her breasts and nipples looked out from the light into the darkness at Hobart like the troubled faces of children.

"I'm coming into the house to explain!" Hobart called to them inside.

"You'll do no such thing! No, no, Hobart!" Lily vociferated back to him, but the intruder dashed away from the window, stumbling over some low-lying bushes, and then presently entered the living room where the preacher was now moaning deeply and beginning even at times to scream a little.

"What on earth possessed you," Lily was beginning to speak when all at once the preacher's mouth fell over hers, and he let out a great smothered roar, punctuated by drumlike rumblings from, apparently, his stomach.

Hobart took a seat near the standing couple.

The preacher was now free of Lily's body at last, and he had slumped down on the floor, near where Hobart was sitting, and was crying out some word and then he began making sounds vaguely akin to weeping. Lily remained with her back and buttocks pressed against the wall, and was breathing hard, gasping indeed for breath. After her partner had quit his peculiar sobbing, he got up and put on his clothes, and walked out unsteadily into the kitchen. On the long kitchen table, the kind of table one would expect in a large school cafeteria, Hobart, from his chair, could spy at least fifteen pies of different kinds, all "homemade" by Lily expressly for the church social which was tomorrow.

He could see the preacher sit down at the big table, and cut himself a piece of Dutch apple pie. His chewing sounds at last alerted Lily to what was happening, and she managed to hurry out to the kitchen in an attempt to halt him.

"One piece of pie isn't going to wreck the church picnic. Go back there and entertain your new boyfriend, why don't you," the preacher snapped at her attempt to prevent him eating the piece of pie.

"He's Edward Starr's brother, I'd have you know, and he's not my boyfriend, smarty!"

The preacher chewed on. "This pie," he said, moving his tongue over his lips cautiously, "is very heavy on the sugar, isn't it?"

"Oh, I declare, hear him!" Lily let the words out peevishly, and she rushed on back into the living room. There she gazed wide-eyed, her mouth trying to move for speech, for facing her stood Hobart, folding his shorts neatly, and stark naked.

"You will not!" Lily managed to protest.

"Who says I don't!" Hobart replied nastily.

"Hobart Starr, you go home at once," Lily ordered him. "This is all something that can be explained."

He made a kind of dive at her as his reply, and pinioned her to the wall. She tried to grab his penis, clawing at it, but he had perhaps already foreseen she might do this, and he caught her by the hand, and then slapped her. Then he inserted his membrum virile quickly into her body, and covered her face with his freely flowing saliva. She let out perfunctory cries of expected rather than felt pain as one does under the hand of a nervous intern.

At a motion from her, some moments later, he worked her body about the room, so that she could see what the preacher was doing. He had consumed the Dutch apple pie, and was beginning on the rhubarb lattice.

"Will you be more comfortable watching him, or shall we return to the wall?" Hobart inquired.

"Oh, Hobart, for pity's sake," she begged him. "Let me go, oh please let me go." At this he pushed himself more deeply upwards, hurting her, to judge by her grimace.

"I am a very slow comer, as you will remember, Lily. I'm slow but I'm the one in the end who cares for you most. Tonight is my biggest windfall. After all the others, you see, it is me who was meant for you. . . You're so cozy too, Lily."

As he said this, she writhed, and attempted to pull out from him, but he kissed her hard, working into her hard.

"Oh this is all so damned unfair!" She seemed to cough out, not speak, these words. "Ralph," she directed her voice to the kitchen, "come in here and restore order. . ."

As he reached culmination, Hobart screamed so loud the preacher did come out of the kitchen. He was swallowing very hard, so that he did remind Hobart of a man in a pie-eating contest. He looked critically at the two engaged in coitus.

A few minutes later, finished with Lily, Hobart began putting on his clothes, yawning convulsively, and shaking his head, while

Ralph began doggedly and methodically to remove his clothing again, like a substitute or second in some grilling contest.

"Nothing more, no, I say no!" Lily shouted when she saw Ralph's naked body advancing on her. "I will no longer co-operate here."

He had already taken her, however, and secured her more firmly than the last time against the wall.

Hobart meanwhile was standing unsteadily on the threshold of the kitchen. He saw at once that the preacher had eaten two pies. He felt un-understandably both hungry and nauseous, and these two sensations kept him weaving giddily about the kitchen table now. At last he sat down before a chocolate meringue pie, and then very slowly, finickly, cut himself a small piece.

As he ate daintily he thought that he had not enjoyed intercourse with Lily, despite his seeming gusto. It had been all mostly exertion and effort, somehow, though he felt he had done well, but no feeling in a supreme sense of release had come. He was not surprised now that Edward Starr had left her. She was not a satisfier.

Hobart had finished about half the chocolate meringue when he reckoned the other two must be reaching culmination by now for he heard very stertorous breathing out there, and then there came to his ears as before the preacher's intense war whoop of release. Lily also screamed and appealed as if to the mountain outside, *I perish! Oh, perishing!* And a bit later, she hysterically supplicated to some unknown person or thing *I cannot give myself up like this, oh!* Then a second or so later he heard his own name called, and her demand that he save her.

Hobart wiped his mouth on the tablecloth and came out to have a look at them. They were both, Lily and Ralph, weeping and holding loosely to one another, and then they both slipped and fell to the floor, still sexually connected.

"Gosh all get out!" Hobart said with disgust.

He turned away. There was a pie at the very end of the table which looked most inviting. It had a very brown crust, with golden juice spilling from fancily, formally cut little air holes, as in magazine advertising. He plunged the knife into it, and tasted a tiny bit. It was of such wonderful flavor that even though he felt a bit queasy he could not resist cutting himself a slice, and he began to chew solemnly on it. It was an apricot, or perhaps peach pie, but final identification eluded him.

Lily now came out into the kitchen and hovered over the big

table. She was dressed, and had fixed her hair differently, so that it looked as if it had been cut and set, though there were some loose strands in the back which were not too becoming, yet they emphasized her white neck.

"Why, you have eaten half the pies for the church social!" she cried, with some exaggeration in her observation of course. "After all that backbreaking work of mine! What on earth will I tell the preacher when he comes to pick them up!"

"But isn't this the preacher here tonight?" Hobart waving his fork in the direction of the other room motioned to the man called Ralph.

"Why, Hobart, of course not. . . He's no preacher, and I should think you could tell. . ."

"How did I come to think he was?" Hobart stuttered out, while Lily sat down at the table and was beginning to bawl.

"Of all the inconsiderate selfish thoughtless pups in the world," she managed to get out between sobs. "I would have to meet up with you two, just when I was beginning to have some sort of settled purpose."

Ralph, standing now on the threshold of the kitchen, still stark naked, laughed.

"I have a good notion to call the sheriff!" Lily threatened. "And do you know what I'm going to do in the morning? I'm going back to Edward Starr in Chicago. Yes siree. I realize now that he loved me more than I was aware of at the time."

The two men were silent, and looked cautiously at one another, while Lily cried on and on.

"Oh, Lily, even if you do go see Edward you'll come home again to us here. You know you can't get the good loving in Chicago that we give you, now don't you?"

Lily wept on and on repeating many times how she would never be able to explain to the church people about not having enough pies on hand for her contribution to the big social.

After drying her tears on a handkerchief which Hobart lent her, she took the knife and with methodical fierce energy and spiteful speed cut herself a serving from one of the still untouched pies.

She showed by the way she moved her tongue in and out of her mouth that she thought her piece was excellent.

"I'm going to Chicago and I'm never coming back!" As she delivered this statement she began to cry again.

The "preacher," for that is how Hobart still thought of him, came over to where Lily was chewing and weeping, and put his hand between the hollow of her breasts.

"No don't get started again, Ralph . . . No!" she flared up. "No, no, no."

"I need it all over again," Ralph appealed to her. "Your good cooking has charged me up again."

"Those pies *are* too damned good for a church," she finally said with a sort of moody weird craftiness, and Ralph knew when she said this that she would let him have her again.

"Hobart," Lily turned to Edward's brother, "why don't you go home. Ralph and I are old childhood friends from way back. And I was nice to you. But I am in love with Ralph."

"It's my turn," Hobart protested.

"No, no," Lily began her weeping again, "I love Ralph."

"Oh hell, let him just this once more, Lily," the "preacher" said. Ralph walked away and began toying again with another of the uncut pies. "Say, who taught you to cook, Lily" he inquired sleepily.

"I want you to send Hobart home, Ralph. I want you to myself. In a bed. This wall stuff is an outrage. Ralph, you send Hobart home now."

"Oh why don't you let the fellow have you once more. Then I'll really do you upstairs." Meanwhile, he went on chewing and swallowing loudly.

"Damn you, Ralph," Lily moaned. "Double damn you."

She walked over to the big table and took up one of the pies nearest her and threw it straight at the "preacher."

The "preacher's" eyes, looking out from the mess she had made of his face, truly frightened her. She went over to Hobart, and waited there.

"All right for you, Lily," the "preacher" said.

"Oh, don't hurt her," Hobart pleaded, frightened too at the "preacher's" changed demeanor.

The first pie the "preacher" threw hit Hobart instead of Lily. He let out a little gasp, more perhaps of surprised pleasure than hurt.

"Oh now stop this. We must stop this," Lily exhorted. "We are grown-up people after all." She began to sob, but very put-on like the men felt. "Look at my kitchen." She tried to put some emphasis into her appeal to them.

The "preacher" took off his jockey shorts, which he had put on a few moments earlier. He took first one pie and then another, mashing them all over his body, including his hair. Lily began to whimper and weep in earnest now, and sat down as if to give herself over to her grief. Suddenly one of the pies hit her, and she began to scream, then she became silent.

There was a queer silence in the whole room. When she looked up, Hobart had also stripped completely, and the "preacher" was softly slowly mashing pies over his thin, tightly muscled torso. Then slowly, inexorably, Hobart began eating pieces of pie from off the body of the smeared "preacher." The "preacher" returned this favor, and ate pieces of pie from Hobart, making gobbling sounds like a wild animal. Then they hugged one another and began eating the pies all over again from their bare bodies.

"Where do you get that stuff in my house!" Lily rose, roaring at them. "You low curs, where do you . . ."

But the "preacher" had thrown one of the few remaining pies at her, which struck her squarely in the breast and blew itself red all over her face and body so that she resembled a person struck by a bomb.

Ralph hugged Hobart very tenderly now, and dutifully ate small tidbits from his body, and Hobart seemed to nestle against Ralph's body, and ate selected various pieces of the pie from the latter.

Then Lily ran out the front door and began screaming *Help! I will perish! Help me!*

The dogs began to bark violently all around the neighborhood.

In just a short time she returned. The two men were still closely together, eating a piece here and there from their "massacred" bodies.

Sitting down at the table, weeping perfunctorily and almost inaudibly, Lily raised her fork, and began eating a piece of her still unfinished apple pie.

# ELEVEN POEMS

## CID CORMAN

1

Mother—dead—
likewise—Dad—
and I the

sedulous
follower.
Evolve, my

soul into
soul. Be
poetry.

2

I open
the window
to let the

air in and
the air in
out. But the

sun—without
more ado—
enters too.


3   COMING TO

Somewhere along the way
something was supposed
to have happened. Perhaps

I read it somewhere.
Or dreamed it.
Anyhow, suddenly, here I

am, at this place,
almost a house—
if there were walls

instead of darkness. I
find myself not
alone. Another man, a

friend perhaps, and I
are seated at
an empty table. Or

is there bread. Or
wine. While wondering
another figure has entered,

joined us, and seems
more familiar to
us than we do

to ourselves. The light
opens near us.
But no shadow falls.

We know the taste
of dying now.
Feed an absence. **Go.**

4

What happens
is. And yet
I say it

and it's gone.
The great *is*
contracted—

a disease—
the sickness
of knowing.

5

I talk. Logic is
illogical, of
course. The largest moon

ripens at the edge
of the earth. We see
our own illusion,

but cherish it no
less. The cul-de-sac
is our whale's belly.

6

Where did you go—or
have I gone—or were
we never here? *Here:*

I touch the paper
or look to where you
must be—to confirm

the illusion of
confirmation. Why
do we masturbate?

7

I walk out of the door into the street
and find myself suddenly *there*. I turn
to look at the opening I have left

only to discover nothing *there*. How
have I become lost between *there* and *there?*
I stoop to lift the shadow at my feet

over this perhaps apparent body,
but it will not be assumed. I must wear
it as it is, pledged, as the light requires.

8

We look for a way
out of words. How lost
can lost be? Thought will

not eliminate
thought, but learns to play
the game of Yoga.

O animal, man,
be the dying you
you alone contain.


9

My friend Samperi
is a god. So small,
however, like the

shape of the breath of
a word, no one sees
where his feeling moves

rises from the page
to enter the lost
city of New York.


10

Delight in knowing
the name of a thing,
knowing a person

by reputation.
Things begin to seem,
as they are sounded,

real. Napoleons,
from your asylums
arise. Your madness

is precisely ours.
But you confuse us
insisting that you

alone are you. All
are Christ and Apollo,
the rose and the sun.


11

As if, if
I didnt
tell you, you

wouldve thought
Hamlet real,
the ghost a

ghost indeed,
at least an
enigma,

or we must
make believe,
suspend, as

the man says,
belief. See
the shadow

of the tree
upon the
tree. Cold night,

silent night,
two men meet
on a roof.

# THE BOY WHO BECAME AN EAGLE

YUMIKO KURAHASHI

*Translated by Samuel Grolmes and Yumiko Tsumura*

One bright holiday afternoon in May, in a glass-wrapped restaurant in a tall building that was floating in the sky, L had a *miai** with a certain young man. She became engaged on the spot.

The sky was exceptionally clear. And when L looked out through the thick glass it was as if there was a nonexistent sea which had lost all flavor of reality. What towered up from the floor of this sea was a jagged metropolis entangled in white neon vines. Below, the cars and people were schools of fish that were playing along the bottom. L was satisfied with everything.

As she thoughtfully let the flavors of all the foods she had placed on her tongue mingle through her mind, and when she had eaten the last of the bacon-wrapped steak, she smiled at the young man and his parents. They immediately returned smiles that were thickly coated with make-up. That things should proceed this way was exactly what L had expected.

L was a student at the university in the Department of Western History. Neither family had objected to scheduling the sumptuous wedding next spring at the time of her graduation.

On that day there will be hordes of people smothered in formal

* The formal meeting at which a man and woman consider becoming engaged to marry.

clothing, and they will all be watching me. In the midst of those luxurious eyes I will officially become this young man's possession. Then my life begins. The everyday life of gentle confinement. A sort of children's game. L sipped the wine and thought, I will get used to everything.

S, the young man who had become her fiancé, had begun his career at a beer company the previous year. His face and body were corpulent, rich. And his father made an equally impressive appearance. They had the brickish red flesh in common; it would have been easy for people to mistake them for brothers. The first time L met them she had dubbed them "the red boars." The nickname did not indicate disdain. To her it was nothing more than a harmless label. Actually, her giving them the name showed the degree to which she was interested.

If she had been asked if she loved S, she would probably have had to ask what the question meant. Is that "the man I am in love with"? The thought would have made her laugh. She could not even locate the capacity for such roles as Fiancé or Husband-to-be in a man such as S. There was no suitable place on this smooth-skinned young man to attach such a label as The Man I Love. Even at the beginning, L had hardly given a thought to the question of who or what sort of man she would marry. She had repeatedly told her mother:

That's no big problem. What I *am* interested in is getting engaged and getting married to some man. And above all, what we should be concerned with is seeing that every effort is made to bring things to that point.

Her mother and grandmother were deeply impressed and felt a childish pleasure in hearing such hard sense from the girl.

The meal ended.

Nothing remained to be discussed in regard to the marriage of L and S. The two fathers and the go-between—they were all important men in the same field of business—dropped their roles of *miai* participants and immediately became stereotyped men of business concerned with abstract opinions about the world of finance. Resounding laughter echoed from their stomachs as testimony that they were indeed men of open-minded, generous nature. Across from them the two mothers began to blossom with words of admiration for the foreign artists who had recently arrived in Japan. L thought the vanity that flicked out of their mouths like little flames resembled a chameleon's tongue darting out at its prey. She wove all ten of her fingers together and pretended to be listening to the conversation with interest. A yawn was swelling up inside her smile. Then she began to stare at S. He did not seem to be conscious of it, so she took an exceptionally long time to lick over the surface of this young man with her eyes.

She thought, He looks like a crab shell.

According to the plan, L and S were to have time alone.

I have tickets to the K Theater, S said.

L had no reason to object. She sat beside him and watched the ritualistic drama; the intertwining of formalized time and space bored her. Her fiancé looked at the stage with a relaxed expression. After the play there was no convenient program guide for their time, so like a pair of ordinary lovers the two of them went to a dark coffee shop. They felt they were in exactly the wrong place. L herself would have preferred a bar, but she hesitated to make the suggestion. S talked about a few things going on at the company, and L talked about her graduation thesis. She was soon bored with the conversation. She did not dislike S, it was just that whatever subject she brought up in front of him made her feel like she was chewing on sand.

This is like I've already lived with the man for twenty years, she thought.

When they parted, S clasped L's outstretched hand, but his was so unusually heavy that it gave her the impression she was supporting a lump of meat.

Shortly afterward, the betrothals were exchanged. Being an officially engaged couple, S and L met from time to time. The pre-arranged plans for the dates were followed point by point. With the confidence of a traveling salesman who had met his quota, S said that he wanted to buy L an engagement ring with his own money.

How would you like a ring with your birthstone? What month were you born in?

October. That's opal.

I'm glad to hear it's October. It would be awful if you had been born in April, S said. He laughed like a junior high school boy. They went immediately to a jewelry store on the Ginza to look at rings.

The engagement ring was placed on her finger. And the next day, in somewhat vulgar taste, L wore that attention-drawing accessory when she went to take part in a student demonstration. This activity was something like parading the streets with a palanquin on a festival day.

I remember once when I was young, a boy about my age fell under one of those palanquins and was crushed like a potato bug. That was a brave and glorious parade. The demonstrations are a little more enthusiastic, but I think they are a bit on the lean side. To take part in one of these you have to have an almost embarrassingly elevated sense of the tragic and pathetic. And above all, you have to have bloodshot eyes.

L was taking part in the demonstration just so she could secretly enjoy the role of a child helping to pull a palanquin around on the street. Besides, she was a member of the Standing Committee from the Humanities Department in the student government. The position helped her consume the time she had so much of.

The demonstration broke up at Shimbashi. When L passed close to Q, he invited her to go have a cup of tea. He was a member of the Standing Committee from the Department of Political Science and Economics. There was a modern jazz coffee shop nearby that stocked the latest imported records. L always went there to relax after the demonstrations. When she suggested that place, Q said that jazz was decadent and that he did not like it. In his case, it was not a stereotyped communist's prejudice; it was nothing more than the characteristic tendency of a poor student from the country to shrink from any luxurious consumption of time and money.

I don't have anything in common with this sort of person, L thought.

What you call labor songs are taken from jazz, and anyway it has a much more earthy feeling than the songs we were singing at the demonstration, L said.

She leaned back into the chair. Her legs were crossed, and she had on skin-tight slacks.

When Q looked at the menu he was surprised by the high prices. L held the conviction that to use the mind for the calculation of money was a disgusting, petty labor. In the first place, she had never known any lack of money, and she was the sort of person who thought the very process of exchanging money for goods was annoying.

Q looked uncomfortable; he leaned forward.

I want to ask you a favor, he said. Can you take over a part-time job for me for a while?

What job? L said vacantly. She was absorbed in the Wes Montgomery "Octave Execution for Guitar."

It's a tutoring job. A high school sophomore, he's not very bright. The demonstrations are going on all the time now, and I just can't make it on the days I'm supposed to. They aren't very happy about it. I'm going to tell them I'm sick and can't make it for a while. Can you take over? Just for a while.

But if you give up the job won't you be short without the money? What are you going to do?

Aw, something will turn up. He laughed to cheer himself up.

L became unpleasant and said, I won't take the money.

Q was puzzled and said, I can't let you do that. But since you feel that way about it, how about letting me borrow half?

All right, L said to end the conversation. I don't have any use for it.

Then Q noticed the ring on L's hand on the table.

What's that? The ring.

I had a *miai* the other day.

And?

It wasn't much fun, but I got engaged.

L knew that Q was privately thinking of himself as her boyfriend. It was a real nuisance to her.

It's always this kind of person, she thought. This domestic animal type of a man. The flow of his imagination is an absolutely shameless secretion.

She ran her eyes over him with a mercilessness in her face that caused Q to drop into an I-am-abused pose. His dirt-smudged throat shook. L thought that it was odd that such a mongrel of a man should be involved in the student movement at all. It was as if an athletic event were being spoiled by the participation of a cripple.

I don't think that we want a mixture of superfluous people, stray dogs, thrusting plans for insidious destruction into the middle of a festival. As far as a student like Q is concerned, wouldn't it be better for him to go on with his part-time job and get some nutrition and give up this sort of activity? L held back this flow of opinion with her gleaming teeth. He would probably come out with a speech like, That's the wrong way to think. If we are going to block the revision of the security treaty, we have to collect all the strength there is, and now, no matter what has to be sacrificed. L was silent. Q gradually revived his decaying spirits, and with his fatigue-yellowed eyes he labeled L a bourgeoise girl who is engaged to a bourgeois man. And then with two or three cynical comments he stood up.

Student life is a long vacation that extends over several years. In L's opinion it was a make-believe life, something, that is, which can only be consumed in play. The job she had been pushed into was no more than the game of keeping company with a proud mother and her stupid son. And in spite of the fact that it was her first experience as a tutor, after she had gone to teach two or three times, she was quite at home with it. The people playing the game were of the same social class as L so she had a thorough knowledge of the rules.

One day L went to dinner with the mother and her children at a restaurant on the Ginza. With a puffy smile that resembled white flower petals, the mother said:

This sort of thing never happened when Q was doing the tutoring.

Q had said that one of the conditions of the job was that there would be a meal included, but for him "meal included" probably meant something like a prisoner eating from a tray that was set in front of him, or the meal you would offer your pet dog, L thought.

She handled her knife and fork gracefully. The mother scolded the boys for their bad table manners while she praised L's model etiquette.

You seem to have been brought up in a very refined home, the mother said. Her voice had the quality of thin steam. L covered her face with a humble smile.

She had only told the mother that she was from a rural area, the daughter of an assistant professor at the university, both a deliberate pretense; but in fact it was obvious to L herself that she was from a much better family than that of her pupil. L generously accepted the mother's flattery. Suddenly, with an astonished look on her face, the mother said:

By the way, wasn't that a terrible thing yesterday? Have you ever been to anything like that?

No, L said without understanding what the woman was talking about.

According to what the mother said, it seemed that a girl had been killed during the demonstration yesterday. Without being critical, the mother was making a variety of exclamations. There were many things to be said, but L merely gestured in the same tone to indicate her abhorrence of such things. She knew the common-sense rule: to refer to the dead more than ritualistically in this sort of place should be avoided.

I suppose a person like Q goes to a lot of demonstrations, don't you think?

I imagine so, L said vaguely. But I really don't know anything about him except that we both came from the same area.

This is a little awkward, the mother said, leaning forward and clasping her thick palms in the air like the statue of a bodhisattva, I don't know what it is, but I just don't feel that I can completely trust K to anyone like Q. And K says the same thing. If it is possible we would like very much to have you continue to be his teacher, permanently.

K nodded agreement, and his ears, which looked like a pair of well formed handles, were dyed the color of blood. He had a perplexed expression on his face. L explained that the agreement she had made with Q was for her to take over only temporarily for him.

As far as that's concerned, I would be more than happy to talk to Q about it myself, the mother said. Whatever we say, this boy. . . . She began to laugh and covered her mouth with her hand, her body shaking. K, she said, just would not be happy with anyone but you. You are such a pretty, gentle young lady. Oh, I'm quite embarrassed. Such a boy! You really are grown up, aren't you, she said.

The mother was teasing K, and at the same time she was quite skillfully placing L high up on a shelf as a young lady who was a model of stability.

K arched his long eyebrows and looked at L to see what her response would be. He was a beautiful boy, and when L recognized that he was in love with her she suddenly found a radiance in him that reminded her of a character out of mythology.

I can give him what he wants, she thought. And she quickly tasted the delicious flavor on her lips. I will become Aphrodite and love this Adonis until he invites his own unnatural death.

L injected K with Love as if she were a doctor attempting an experiment in dissecting a living body. She cauterized his eyes, made an incision on his stomach. The boy's body was saturated with shame and fear and arrogant desire. L took great pleasure in watching the ferocious growth of these things. Like a beautiful youth of Roman descent whose physical beauty is increased by his very lack of intelligence, K was a boy whose survival, whose only reason for existence was the privilege he gained from his beautiful face. For L his confession of and talk about love was all accomplished through his exquisite body. Words, the words which would blow away the compact sense of existence were unnecessary. For example, when L looked into the boy's face as she pressed back his burning hands with the flat of her cold palms, his skin was like a smooth, rose-colored porcelain; it contained a superb brilliance of expression which held a shadow that was reflected from somewhere outside of him rather than from within his inner self. His eyes that were ornamented with plantlike lashes, his quivering fruitlike lips, his tongue—L appreciated, deciphered them.

The boy wanted L.

Maintaining the dignity of Aphrodite, L gently drew the boy toward her by the back of his neck, and gave him her lips. She granted him the prize of an instant's taste and withdrew.

Hmmm. That will be all today. If you study hard I'll give you a reward again. So, let's increase the vocabulary quota. Memorize all the words from F to H for the next time.

During the following month, while she gave him her body little by little, L gradually enveloped him in Love, in the way she might have gone about taming some rare beast. The boy was as obedient inside his cage as a noble giraffe. With the exception of an occasional entwinement of his fingers in hers or in her hair, he did not refuse to remain an object of propriety beneath L's petting. And his grades on the semester examinations in July were conspicuously improved. His gleaming eyes pleaded for a reward. L hugged him tightly. It was a long embrace because it was a special reward, and also because it was to cherish the regret of having to part for the summer vacation. It was the first time K's strong vinelike arms had held that part of L's torso which so compressed. He made L let out a short, musical scream.

With the excuse that she was returning to her family home in the country for a few weeks, L received a leave from K's mother, and with her own mother, her sister and her little cousins she left for E shoreline on the outer Boso Peninsula.

She was consuming the summer in the midst of the sand and the indigo sea, and the huge anvil clouds and the excessive light that could burn the earth. One morning in August along a deserted shore while L was wading for shrimp and sea urchins, K appeared suddenly, wrapped in a white linen shirt. L had told him in secret where the rented villa on the E shoreline was.

Look! I've found an urchin, L said.

K stood silently staring at her nearly naked body with the eyes of a vulture. She tossed back her wet black hair from her shoulders and offered him her lips.

What happened?

Mother said I could go to Oku-Nikko to study with you.

Oh! Wonderful!

L threw her wet body into the boy's arms. He was standing at a slight angle and he had a perplexed look on his face.

They left the seaside and went back to Tokyo and then headed for Nikko, north along the Kanto Plain, which had been burned a dusty white by the dry weather. The reserved coach "Nikko" was pleasant.

It's just like we're on a honeymoon trip, L thought.

In the sunglasses and summer suit that L had secretly bought for him, her young "husband" was an impersonation of a clean gentleman. But the smile on his rosy lips was that of such a young boy that at times it bewildered L. Having such excellent material in front of her made L's heart tighten with the joy that a sculptor who molds things with his fingers and palms would feel.

Darling, that hat looks a little funny on you. You're not wearing it right.

L adjusted the hat and pushed back a soft lock of hair that fell over his forehead. The boy curled his lips and made a pompous nod.

They were enthusiastic, and on their way to Oku-Nikko they went to see the temple compound of Toshogu and the Kegon Falls. They had a meal of fried rainbow trout at the lake by Chuzenji Temple, and then they took a taxi to Lake Yu-no-ko. The road went through forests of white birch and larch, and gradually ascended across the Senjo-ga-hara Plain, which was already showing the lonely, deserted features the decline of summer brought. L shrieked as she pointed out Mr. Nantaisan on their right where it squatted in a huge masculine bulk.

Look! Doesn't it feel "massive," she said, using the English word. It looks almost like a lie. Hey, do you know how to say "massive" in Japanese?

K had a grown-up look on his face, and he smiled.

You are some scholar, L said with an exaggerated sigh.

The dry leaves on the trees in the forest were white with powder, and as the taxi drove by it was engulfed in its own huge cloud of dust.

They arrived at the Hotel N. Their bags were already there. According to plan, K addressed L as his wife, and although his voice was a little shaky, he talked with the manager tactfully. In the room L loosened K's necktie and teased him.

How does it feel to be a husband?

Wouldn't Mother be surprised if she could see us now, K said.

He stood passively while L took off his clothes and dressed him in a *yukata.** When the maid came in and offered to show them to the bath, K became ill tempered, like a boy who hates bathing would act peevishly toward his mother. He insisted that he did not want to go into the bath with L.

Are you bashful?

I'm not bashful, he said. His cheeks puffed as if he were pouting deliberately, and they turned a beautifully shy pink. We can't, we're not supposed to do things like that.

L petted him gently on the neck.

Fraidy cat! Okay then, you go on and get in first.

No. You'll come in before I'm out.

When K left, L collected her thoughts as she changed into a *yukata.*

I am all right, aren't I?

Her uneasiness made her hesitate.

I have to carry everything off perfectly. I must create that dramatic moment with the aesthetic attitude of an obscene, noble queen who devours a black slave with shining skin every night after her banquet.

If anything goes wrong, I will have to kill him, L murmured.

Suddenly she remembered Q. Then the thought of her appointed marriage to the red boar put her in high spirits.

This is a breach of promise, she said liltingly.

The boy was standing like a statue in the large bathroom, and the room was full of steam and the odor of sulphur. His back was toward L, and it expressed a dismay that bordered on fury. She undressed, and when she held her breasts against the boy's broad, smooth back, it offered only a weak refusal. He was erect and quivering.

* A cotton kimono for lounging or wearing after the bath. It is customary for a hotel or inn to furnish one for each guest.

Turn around, L pleaded gently and tickled him under the ear.

No, the boy said and he jerked his shoulders.

But L's arms had surrounded him, and like an insect-eating plant devouring its prey she had enticed his being and emasculated it. K immediately weakened. In L's arms he had lost all his freedom. She easily rotated the statue and thrust her breasts against his chest. Her hand immediately slid down the trunk and grabbed the only firm branch securely.

You're fresh, she murmured.

And she confirmed her hand's possession of the boy's cylinder of burning shame. K wiggled. His very being was entrapped, confiscated by L's hand, and his body was a slave that could not break the chains no matter how violently he might struggle against them. When L's hand released him, he slid down the column of complicated curves and kneeled with his arms around her hips. L was calm. For some reason the boy did not have any eyes. It was impossible for him to look at L at a time like this. L laughed and told him he had permission to do anything he wanted to. His face rubbed up into her, and his hands reached up to hold the heavy fruitlike meat of her breasts from below. The innocent yet noble dissoluteness that a properly raised boy shows once he strips himself of a sense of shame is astounding. Once K had completely exposed himself to L, he lost all inclination to hide anything, and began to act with a boldness that resembled a child at play in the sand on the seashore. L washed his body. Then the two of them played in the big bath to their hearts' content.

It was already dark outside. The standard hotel meal of crisp slices of raw carp, salted trout and broiled eel was served. They both had huge appetites. K guzzled the beer.

After dinner they took a walk by the lakeside. The black surface of the lake glittered like a sharp blade in the bottom of a pail of cold air. The shore was deserted. According to what the maid had told them all the inns had been crowded with students of the open-air summer schools until recently. But now all the inns around this area were only dotted with lighted rooms. Holding on to each other like lovers, L and K sat in a boat that had been dragged onto the shore and kissed each other until they grew tired of it.

It's cold, L said, and she rubbed her head against the boy's chest as if she were trying to find a cave somewhere to crawl into.

You can really tell this is fifteen hundred meters above sea level, K said. Let's go back and go to bed before we catch cold.

There was no trace of summer remaining in the cold twilight, and wrapped in the common thought of warming themselves together naked in bed, L and K returned to the Hotel N.

A particular talent is necessary for two people to be able to love each other. According to L it was not strength of imagination, but rather it had to be the fine expression of an ordinary imagination through the body. Excess of passion spoils the technique. L petted the boy. Where her hand stroked him, he became even more naked, a substance of extreme purity, complete flesh itself. L's eyes searched, and her tongue followed where they had been. She added language to the pleasure of this conquest, naming each part of his body. The phallic rose banana, the handle of being, the knob. The broad plain of his chest. The legs that extend to the world's end. The fragrant summer grass. L possessed them all. Each was an exquisite *objet*. She knew that she made an obscene picture, reigning naked over this *objet* and indulging herself so in the petting.

My own body is gross flesh that flaps and quivers all by itself. If K were to open his eyes and even glance at me, I would be nothing but an indecent naked woman inviting his hatred. He would stamp on me. Desire is a ferocious self-tyranny that devours obscenity itself.

The boy gradually learned his role beneath L's petting. Then the roles reversed. L offered her sacrificial flesh to the boy's sight. He twisted and ripped at the still living and moving victim; he was callowly trying to push L's leaking consciousness back into her flesh. L gave up her freedom. She was thrown to the floor as if her arms and legs were bound. Her only consciousness was the shame that pierced her body like a hot sword. Suddenly, she opened her eyes. Then she felt the release. Now, I am free, she felt. Her hand, an accomplice, helped the boy in his unskilled loving.

The pain calmed her completely. And in that pain L herself became an *objet*. She screamed softly to let the boy know that he had secured her completely. She felt wonderful.

It's a success! she knew.

She leaned her head on the boy's chest and talked on and on in a whisper.

How was I? she asked.

You're wonderful, K said and petted her hair. The way he said it had a firmness that deliberately treated L as his Lover.

He probably thought I was an obsessed woman. Most boys who have an older woman as their first experience have the impression that they have been insulted, just sampled mercilessly.

I was a virgin, could you tell? L said.

L made love to the boy from morning till night. His beautiful exterior was her fascination.

I am making love to him like a sodomite, she thought. Wouldn't it be wonderful if I were the man.

She imagined possessing this beautiful boy in an act of sodomy with herself in the man's role.

That is probably my ideal love, she thought.

The sun at the close of summer was weak now, but it still scattered warm light that was a hot golden powder during the day. L put K in the boat and they floated around the lake. She ordered him to take off all his clothes. He obeyed. He acted like a young girl who knew nothing but subjugation after having been deprived of everything. Only his well-formed body had the appearance of the sturdiness that was manly, and in fact it was a counterfeit. The false masculinity in all its imaginable luxurious beauty, the body covered with useless muscles shone like gold in the over-pouring sunshine. L manipulated the oars softly to avoid those places where the mountains fell into the lake to spread shadows that were like death, and she steered the boat toward the summer that barely remained at the center of the lake. When another boat approached, she casually draped a large bath towel over the boy to hide his nakedness.

The summer vacation ended. L took K back to Tokyo. His appearance was totally changed by the more than ten days of play. K looked at his lover with melancholy eyes. He was an ordinary young man who had become slightly worm-eaten by dark shadows.

I guess his mother is sure to see the change. Those wise, elephant eyes of hers will see through everything in an instant.

L made K swear to keep their secret, but it would be futile.

Listen, I'm only your temporary teacher, you know, so I won't be teaching you in September.

I don't want you to, the boy shouted in a stubborn tone.

What do you mean, you don't want me to?

I don't want you to quit.

In K's extremely sullen face L saw the expression of a man's frustration at the limitations of love. She quickly became cold, and with a slight shrug of her shoulders she thought:

This is not how I wanted things to turn out.

She said, Well, what do you want?

I don't want you to go away, I love you.

But if we go on like this, you'll end up being a papa. How would you like that?

L chose cruel words and she stabbed them into his chest like needles. But K understood them as insults and threats and with a ferocious look in his eyes he said:

You can't threaten me. If you really are going to have a baby, I'll take care of you.

Don't worry, don't worry, L said, unable to hold back a laugh. If it came to that the whole thing would be absolutely ridiculous.

But L was sure that would never happen.

The fact that Q did not come back to Tokyo in September became an excuse for prolonging the relationship between L and K. L thought she could make use of this prolongment as a period in which to retame K and then gradually draw away from him. This was a complete miscalculation.

I won't be tricked by anything like that, K declared.

His cunning had developed to a degree that it equaled his stubbornness. The medical therapy technique of gradually tapering off after a period of total indulgence did not work with K. He persisted forcefully in his desire to have complete freedom with L's body. One afternoon L relented and took K to a lover's hotel for a few hours.

The next time, Q is going to do the tutoring. Let's make this the last time, L said tenderly.

Just hearing Q's name made K frown. It was raw jealousy. Somehow K knew that both L and Q were members of committees in the student government and that they were both active participants in the student movement. He persisted in suspecting that their relationship was more than friendly. It was possible that Q had once said something of the sort to him. L was fed up.

Since things have turned out this way, there is no choice but for me to quietly disappear, she concluded.

One morning at around the time the fallen ginkgo nuts on the campus had begun to emit a foul odor, L ran into Q in front of the library.

When did you get back? L said. You're awfully late. Were you working on the movement back home too?

Yeah, a little bit, Q said. His sunken cheeks were taut. It was a waste of time, though. Nobody would listen, not even when I was talking about the treaty. And those farmers, they say the students up here in Tokyo just don't have anything to do and that's why we make a fuss about things. They say that nobody has any intention of coming back home to help with the farming, but that when we get a vacation we come back and preach sermons about all sorts of complicated things.

Isn't that about the truth? L said very casually. Anyway, what do you intend to do about the tutoring arrangements?

I want you to let me take over again, of course, Q said.

All right. I don't know if the mother wants you back or not, but at any rate, I am quitting.

Hearing this, Q bared his dirty gap-teeth. He complained that that was because L probably let something slip to the mother about his being active in the student movement. L was astounded, and she denied it.

Even without my saying anything, the mother is smart enough to sense that much, she said.

Aw, you've made a mess of things, Q said. He began methodically grinding up the ginkgo nuts at his feet.

I've still got to find a job for after graduation.

Yes, I know, find a job . . . , L repeated, but it was a subject about which she had absolutely no concern.

If you have to just get a job and work and eat, it would be better to be dead, she thought.

The concept of people making a living depressed L. Q tediously began explaining what his situation was.

No matter what, I've got to get a job, he said.

And his face was twisted with a tenacity so strong that it made his words sound almost like threats.

He told her that even the tutoring could turn out to be a good connection. L was angry.

She said, Why do you make me listen to such stuff.

Q's face fell and he looked as if he were going to cry.

Will you ask your father for me, too, he said. His voice had no confidence in it.

And then one by one she pointed out the inappropriate conditions that Q was trailing behind him. His family ran a rural variety store, he had no father, he had been arrested once as the leader of a demonstration.

And on top of all that, you probably don't have good grades, do you? Are you getting any credits? If you can't pass the on-campus screening, there's no way to use connections anyway. So, I definitely will not ask him.

I think I can get by without the student movement thing coming out. Anyway I'm completely clear of it now . . . There was a touch of nostalgia in his voice.

You had better be, L said.

She was thinking, In the first place it's wrong for a student like you to get involved in the student movement at all. It's just like it would be to enroll in the athletic department. You need time and money and strength to do it.

A few days later, L ran into Q in the cafeteria, and he told her that he had gotten his part-time job back and asked her once more to get him an appointment with her father so he could ask his help in finding a position. L laughed and refused. Q stood up with the spoon from his curry rice still in his hand. He stared at her with hatred, and as if he was trying to rip out the words that clogged in his throat, he cursed at her and called her a repulsive bourgeoise:

How would you like it if S was informed of your affair with K?

Ah, informed . . . It wouldn't shock me, she said. Her own fascination with the word produced a slight shudder in her. That word "informed" was pasted to Q like a thin rubber mask and he looked like the personification of baseness.

To make your baseness glow a little brighter, you should inform the police about the student movement, L said cheerfully and left the cafeteria.

On a windy Saturday in October, L ran into S on the Ginza for the first time in a month. Unexpectedly, it was L who invited S to go to the modern jazz coffee shop in Yurakucho, and he followed her, carrying himself proudly, walking behind her like some stately guard. The coffee shop was filled with students. When L sat down she thought she saw K in a student uniform at the busy doorway, and standing behind him the figure of Q.

If it is K, he must have followed me at Q's instigation.

L felt a little excited. The boy sat down on a chair in the corner with his neat back toward L. She did not see the man who looked like Q who had been standing behind him. She disliked the embarrassing drama called confession, but nevertheless she thought it was necessary to come to a certain degree of understanding with her fiancé, so she brought up the subject.

Do you know a man named Q?

No, I don't, S answered clearly. It did not sound like a lie.

Then, in a happy tone, as if she were retelling some fairy story, L explained:

I have been threatened by a man named Q. But the basis of the threat is the truth. However, no matter how many lovers I have had relations with, it has absolutely nothing to do with you. So if you are bothered by that kind of thing, there is nothing for us to do but break off the engagement.

S listened as if he were deeply interested, but with a generous smile he said:

I'm not bothered by it at all. And of course you know I have had a lot of affairs myself. If you're interested I would be happy to tell you about them.

They put their foreheads together and merrily began telling each other about their affairs. They acted like two old people who had regained their juvenile innocence. L was amazed at the thickness of S's mask.

This man! she thought. He's got such a fine reputation as a real company man, but in spite of being a red boar, all this that he is telling me sounds like the truth.

When they stood up they exchanged smiles.

Maybe you ought to date this K fellow from time to time if you want to, S said and pushed open the twilight-colored glass door.

They went out into the street. It was bustling with the wind and the people.

Just then a black figure knocked L aside and lunged into S. The scream "It's K!" formed in L's mouth. For just an instant she thought that K had become an eagle. His glossy black wings spread and the eagle jumped on S, his flashing talons were like a silver blade. By the time L had gathered her senses, she knew what was happening. Slowly, the boy moved the arm that was holding the knife; it was a motion like the starting movement of a piston. The knife gouged S twice, once in the chest and once in the side. S's chest thrust out and his hands came together, moving almost mystically, and his fingers clasped in front of his chest like a statue of Buddha. There was no resistance to the stabbing. L watched him fall over. He had a slightly puzzled look on his face.

This is exactly like being on a movie set, L thought.

A large number of people had stopped, and their eyes formed a crowd around the scene. L stood immobile like the heroine of a movie as she endured this crack of unreality that was suddenly opening in front of her. The boy swiftly turned his insane, bloodshot eyes on L. They were no longer K's eyes.

At that instant, L thought she saw the form of Q behind this eagle. The base manipulator of the ferocious eagle, the informer. The boy lunged at her, and inside a fence of human beings L's long scream rose.

# SIX POEMS FROM
# *IMAGINARY BEINGS*
# *OF THE WILL*

A. POULIN, JR.


## THE ELEPHANT'S WOMB

*to Daphne*

A school of bright yellow and orange fish
swims above your bed. I wake up on land,
remembering and afraid, gasping for breath.
Your pink pig stands on its hind legs,
begging for pennies that shorten his life.
Monkeys swing from the wood of their elbows,
the knots of their eyes staring into mine.
The square elephant's head you made and were
one day has taken your room for its body.
Her eyes shining from another world fill up
with darkness, and I walk out of her side,
anxious to see you, anxious to see you are
still my daughter. Tonight before you fall
asleep, or some other when you wake, screaming,
I'll tell you how we all must move from one
kingdom of beasts to another, and another,
how each is more treacherous than the last,
and what we all have to strangle to survive.

## JINNS

Wingless, the babies scratch
in the corner shadows, their skin
shredded into fur. They snap
at my ankles, their eyes fierce
as knotholes in the sunlight
burning the walls of old barns.
If I look into them, I can see
the horror of my most private
hope. I climb the attic stairs.
Filling the sudden explosion of
dark, the shapeless memory of un-
remembered guilt, a terrible angel.
He raises one calm wing up to a beam,
and with the other gently offers me the rope.

## MERMAIDS

They spawned us in our father's first
wet dreams, then outlived them
and the memory of pleasure thwarted
by the threat of sons. Now they surface
to the bright brim of our own loneliness:
strangers cracking the porcelain
of our teeth with the unsatisfied hope
for a feeling we would die for.

Water breaks. Words dissolve in the salt
of their own horror waking up: Mother!
Naked, her shoulders cold and green
as kelp, she swims toward me. The hair
on her body, head, the hair that divided
for my head, shining, iridescent scales
in the watery blue. Her mouth hunts mine,
open, singing from and toward another
and more lasting life. The moon rocks
us to sleep on a bed of pure white sand.

Hair divides again, the sea muscadines,
and I slip into that deeper, lasting
sleep no man returns from or wants to.


## LUBAS

Disguised as shapes you love, lovers, friends,
and wives, they are the princes of beasts.
You never learn to fear them or wage war
against them until they're just about to kill you.
Instead, you believe you're the creature
that they say you are. When your friend says
your right hand hurts him, cut it off.
Tear out your tongue: it can never please
your lover. Give your children your eyes.
Here, love, eat the heart of my last hope.


## SEA MONKEYS

Fertilized by water, each pebble grows
its own arms and legs, a head, and bright
infinitesimal genitals that are sterile.
They tumble in the jungle of artificial
grass and dream of their children chattering
in the palms. One morning, all my fathers
and brothers have risen into the air.


## MIRROR-FISH

At the vanishing point of the mirror's depth
of field, there's a shining, shifting fish.
In the bright sun or dark of sleep, it swims

in the blue of my cornea. Sometimes a tiger,
its color like no color, it comes ringed
with the clatter of weapons. This fish is
the first to come back from the improbable
land of mirrors. Prisoners of lead, condemned
to be repetitions of our dreams and acts,
they're beginning to stir now, to contradict
the angle of my finger, color of a scar.
Tusks defy my teeth. Hooves trample my hair.
Tonight the sea is churning with the cries
of all its secret creatures, and the vague,
distant, but familiar outline of a man walks
toward the center of my eye. Free again,
they're coming back. Tomorrow morning I'll point
a revolver at my face, and, knowing who will win,
one reflection will kill the other and survive.

# NEW ORLEANS INTERMISSION

AL YOUNG

1

I see it zooming down
over the Bayou late April
morning of the brightest green
from the window of a jet named Nancy

Settling back childishly
in the sky all alone,
my secret hand waves light aside
to get a better look at
all the music coiling up
inside me again as I watch
this still virgin landscape

Is that the famous Mississippi
down there, are those the streets
Jelly Roll did his marching,
strutting & poolsharking in?
Was I really just born

a Gulf away from here or
carved like Pinocchio from
some thick dark tree below?


2

The only way to love a city's
to live in it til you know
every door every store every
parkingmeter deadlawn alleycat
district smell pussy hotel
gumwrapper & wino by heart

Airborne all night my sleepy heart
leaps like windblown raindrops

I'm a very old baby re-entering
an unchanged world with a yawn


3

Yes Ive lived here before
just as I know & can feel in my tongue
that Ive tramped this earth as
storyteller & unaccountable thief
too many times before,
a displaced lover of spirit & flesh

Riding the St Charles trolley nights
an old American, classically black,
spots me as tourist & softly explains
how he dont have to take snapshots
no more since he can more or less
picture in his mind what's keepable

When I take this 15¢ ride, the cool
off hour breeze tightening my skin,
I can tune in to people telling their
stories real slow in the form of asides

& catch myself doing a lot of smiling
to hold back tears.

      Oldtimer tells me
why the fare on this line's so cheap:
"It's so the colored maids & cooks &
gardeners can git to they jobs & back
without it bein a strain on they pocket"


4


On Bourbon Street (North Beach or
Times Square) a fantailed redhead in
G-string & nothing else waves me
into a topless/bottomless joint with a
dogfaced barker posted at the door
who yips & howls: "C'mon in yall & see
southron gals takin off they draws
for just the price of a drink!"

        It isnt
enough to laugh & rush in like a
prospective drunk that's in heat.

The point is that love & love alone
holds up my feet as they step from
Bourbon to Rampart Street, dreaming of
Congo Square, Creole intrigue, Fats
Domino & Dr John while a black hippie
(cross between Satchmo & Papa John Creech)
hits on me for 50¢ in front of Al Hirt's


5


Steaming hot down in front of us now:
ham/biscuit eggs grits cajun coffee
& a solid glass of buttermilk for me
for fun—

It's Mom's in the morning
where American poet Miller Williams
leans past his dark wife Becky to say:
"You probly the only Californian that
really knows about this place, man!"

I know I'll slip back by for gumbo
for lunch known down here as a dinner,
or for a supper of 90¢ crawfish bisque

But right now it's the light quivering
in from the street down onto our plates
that makes us quit talking poetry

"I'd give up writing," Miller sighs,
"if I could sing as good as Ray Charles"

Tomorrow theyll drive back to the Ozarks
Tomorrow I'll fly back to California
where there're no nickel phonecalls,
pick up the show from where I left off
& read Marie LeVeau the Voodoo Queen

(New Orleans/San Francisco 1972)

# FIRST PERSON BIOGRAPHY

An excerpt from the novel *Island People*

COLEMAN DOWELL


I

What do we call those memories which strike forcefully, usually toward our sleep though sometimes as flashes of lightning, when we, like the storm, are at a peak of activity?

I don't mean the *déjà vu*, which in its pure form surely is one of the most excruciating experiences one can have ('pure form' here meant to set it apart from those popular, slightly melancholy and romantic sensings which are decent enough to be sung about). I have known the real thing only once, and when it was over I prayed that I might never know it again, for during the seizure, which was I imagined like epilepsy, I thought my brain would burst.

The memories to which I refer are patently unreal; even in the throes, watching details unfold around the catalyst, we know that they are unreal, yet their reality is strong enough by comparison to overshadow the real objects framing the aperture through which we perceive the memory.

One recent day, seated at my desk trying to write, offended by the cheerless post—catalogs, one bill—I looked around my writing room and saw: on the Apollo, my silver wig, which constricts my thoughts so that I cannot work in it, though it was meant to free me from my own dark brown 'reality' with intimations of eighteenth-century courts; under the northwest window, the two-gallon gray pottery crock, blue painted butterfly, blue painted '2,' filled with slowly knotting chrysanthemums; gluttony too was in the room visibly in the remains of my obese sandwich which hunger had forced me to eat, at an hour earlier than my schedule advises; and danger was in the room, the danger of my own obesity, for I realized all at once how far one can be pushed by extended panic, and in what direction mine was pushing me. Between the wigged Apollo and the chrysanthemums there is a space of wall with a bookcase spilling its guts, bulging toward the floor in an excrescencelike bellying, with six "Virginia Quarterlies" and four Virginia Woolf's, unplanned companions, fallen onto the floor; and next to the bookcase there is the northeast window. Framed in its lower sash, in the lower middle pane slightly right of the brass handle, is the tub of succulents which sits on the hemisphere of grass between the half circle of graveled drive and the road, under the two maples which I have named Philemon and Baucis. The tub is canker-green, the succulents a bit yellower than would be served by 'pallid,' a word one wants anyhow to use about them.

On either side of the framing pane are the white-fringed curtains that identically mask the jambs of the room's six windows. On five of the windows the curtains on their wooden rings are generally kept folded back into narrow panels, but this one window, the northeast window, is, once the trees have dropped their leaves, kept two-thirds blind mainly because of the view of my bare backside its openness would afford to passers-by as I practice those more elongated poses (*Suryanamaskar, Sirshasana, Sarvangasana*) of my two-hour daily Yoga.

My eyes traveled from hyacinthine wig to chrysanthemums, noting the similarity that was made utterly uncharming because of another factor—age—that caused an equal though hidden dissimilarity: the wig was practically new, hyacinthine by recent design, but it capped the Apollo at least partly because of my age, whereas the chrysanthemums in their age actually resembled me— falling petals, organic shrinkage—and so the surface likeness between the two objects became confusing enough to be maddening. Then my eyes in traveling passed over and returned to the succulents, and memory poured into the room on such a flood, involving all the senses, that I was affronted by the excess.

Later I tried to write about the experience, and it fell into more or less metered form (I am no poet), and once it was put down I forgot it, or thought I did, and it was today that I found the fragments, which made me recall that I had dreamed the experience solidly into my past, woven it there quite firmly, so that reading the fragments was like discovering an old letter long sought.

One fragment:

> The grass browning toward sleep
> Like a child met halfway
> By his dream of fur.

Another:

> But through cracked fringed curtains
> Potted succulents are coffined
> As to a child's horrored gaze carried upon
> Midnight feet to the parlor
> (The last twisting leaves of bright maple
>     the shuddering candleflames)

Followed by:

> Slice memory there like meat;
> Show the tendons but stay
> The feast.

In the 'poem'—three or four pages of long lines, many of them prose-long—there is a past, the past of someone I do not know and have never known, someone who dwells in a country I have never seen that is filled with carefully detailed artifacts and landscape features unrecognizable to me though now I know them well—and, in fact, knew them well when first I saw them, so that 'recognition' must either expand for me and encompass something for which I have no word, or must cease to have any meaning.

For immediacy, I have written as though the experience were virgin: "must either expand . . . or must cease to have any meaning . . . ," but I have so many of these nonmemory memories that what was mine and what this other person's, or those other people's, is a thing I cannot answer for. I sometimes believe that I can recall when—those occasions on which—the nonmemories struck me with such force as to seem a form of rape, but I have no way to prove that I am not imagining this about one of my 'legitimate' times past, any more than I can prove the converse. Therefore I may be entirely artificial, or entirely 'real,' as well as many mixtures of each.

What intrigues me most is the possibility that I 'exist' only at those times when I am in the throes of a seizure, so that the 'reality' (sorry about those endless quotes but they seem the simplest method) preceding and succeeding the seizure, framing it, as I have said earlier, is part of the seizure too. Then the room that I think I work in, and the house, land, country have only brief existence in the roles of frames, or supernumeraries. The house that I can describe to you in all its rooms and their details, below stairs and above, may not occupy any space but the space in my head. Perhaps this room only floats here, and the maples and the pot of succulents are pasted there in front in a narrow panel, and what I see, think I see, from the other five windows is either clever *trompe l'oeil* or a series of nonmemories like fireworks, exploding and disappearing quietly as I turn this way and that.

To find yourself unable to prove or disprove anything is a kind of freedom, perhaps not one sought, but then, neither is birth.

I was born, they tell me, in the house of my godmother on the banks of a green river.

Except on occasions when reminders to myself may be necessary, I will dispense with the tiresome quotation marks to frame ironies, as well as with such by now obvious qualifiers as 'I think,' 'they tell me,' 'if,' and so on. I shall be henceforth as deliberate in the writing of this biography as though I were certain of its events, bolstered and supported by rafts of letters, documents, and verbal recountings. But as I do not know myself from the inside I shall continually think of this as biography; let it be then a first-person biography, with 'I' as a convenient artifact.

I was born in the house of my godmother on the banks of a green river. I was photographed at nine months in possession of a hairbrush I had stolen. In the photograph I am held by a smiling five-year-old boy, my brother, and am flanked by two sisters, one considerably older than the other children in the photograph, maternally smiling. The other sister is a small solemn creature of three. Another sister is missing from the photograph as she is missing from life, being the first of us to have died. One sister is missing because unborn.

I do not have the photograph nor a copy for this reason: it was lost on its way to be copied so that we all might have a piece of the record. Do the others feel as I do, that the loss was as serious as the loss of a memory bank? though I do not think so because of all the others there are many photographic records, whereas that was the only one of me between birth and the age of fourteen. I do not know why this is so. My suspicions are infinite.

Thus I look at the photograph with my mind's eye, which I visualize nastily as being like a stylus that rapidly scans with its single eye the disclike records of my life; a stylus in a groove, or a beam of light, is sanitary and unobjectionable, but the image of eye-on-a-stalk revolts me and goes with me always, and if it looms up when I am in the midst of fellatio I cannot proceed.

I look at the photograph and wonder what features might be discernible in the plump child that could point to pederasty, and late bigotry, and interim beauty, as well as to the precipice where I cling now between twice daily trips to the post office, having put all other life at a distance, requiring that our communications be through the mails.

On Saturday last I murdered a boy, nineteen years old, radiant as Apollo, and unless I confess no one will ever know. Where, in the recalled photograph of the plump safe child, is the contour or line, or current between siblings, or between children and missing parents—that, even to a master, even to God, might indicate that murder in the future?

Of course it is necessary to tuck in one of my reminders here (should I write 'reminders' and break all vows?) that the memory of the murder could be a nonmemory, but this morning (another nonmemory perhaps) I rang the number he had given me and heard the anxiety and fear in a woman's voice. It was a mature voice, so maybe she was Hap's mother. On the other hand, it is possible that he has sisters as I had who are much older; so it could have been an anxious sister.

What I did was ask for Hap, and hastily, because it was early in the morning, add that I did not under any circumstances desire that he be awakened if he was—and I laughed—unconscious. The laugh was a theatrical touch, neither nervous nor cruel by intent; actually it was spontaneous, and I felt ashamed immediately afterward. What I had meant to do was try to sense what his environment might be like; voices are eloquent, especially when fearful; and I had meant to sound mature, it was essential that I sound *older,* for I have an adolescent's voice, and I suppose I meant to try to sense what his being missing might mean.

My diary was found by a sister who spread it about among the family that I was in love with a male teacher, and thus the designation 'abnormal' entered my life before puberty did. It was a curious entrance, not a conventional pain at all as when nails and sharded glass and jealousy entered me. There was no sharpness, but rather a crowding, like fur in the throat. The diary was, of course, found, but the word 'abnormal' was truly a found word, for I had been searching for it, had dreamed toward sleep of finding it, knowing that when I did I would know I had.

I had of course encountered the word, for I read incessantly, but its application to me had not occurred; Kraft-Ebing, on the printed page, lay in the future. Encountering words that are descriptive of oneself is a varied experience; it is only then that they become personal, entering us as part of our matter, but the method of entry is various and can be as simple as inwardly riding a caught breath or as complex as emptying Oedipus' eye-socket of its eye.

'Fellatio' is like a banjo tune, lively as a jig; I encountered it years too late, in a spritely mood, and laughed all the way over the top. 'Beautiful' was strange and solemn, like the Scriabin *étude* that measured the word into my life, but of course it is meaningless now, both as applies to me and to its place in the language. Beautiful is not beautiful, it has been superseded by blackness and gayness and extreme situations, many of them pornographic, many of them cruel, many of them as meaningless as the word beautiful.

At a party in the reign of Claudo I was voted out of a fairly formidable assemblage most beautiful, and now hindsight and not a nonmemory informs me that I had been voted most meaningless, because of what has happened to the word.

But the plump child in the photograph was merely uninteresting; the stolen hairbrush was the focal point of the child; his hands attract only because they hold the brush. The other three children were infinitely more pleasing to see—the gleeful five-year-old, the maternally smiling heavy-haired fourteen-year-old sister, the serious three-year-old creature with the luminous eyes. But it is a word, eventually, that dominates the photograph and the word is of course 'stolen.' It is the aura, the interest, actually the reason for the visit to the photographer's studio, for those were not the days of the home snapshot.

Thus before I could talk (in the photograph, I now recall, the tongue lolls suspiciously idiot-large, swollen; has mother's hand only a moment before withdrawn from the camera's range carrying my drool on a handkerchief?)—before I could utter, my life had been entered by a word, 'stolen'; by extension, surely, 'little thief' as epithet for me was in the photograph, in the air, in my life. But as I have no memory of the deed, the words, the session in the studio, what results is that an actual occurrence of real import and influence becomes my first nonmemory. It presents itself to me framed by artifacts and the words of others, but it is patently unreal.

I go on at such length because it was the first event in my life considered important enough to have been recorded upon film, and the last such event until, at age fourteen, I won a contest. But it was the school I attended to which (to whom) the award was important enough for a photograph, therefore the only occurrence important enough to assume its place among the sea of family records was my act of theft, and in this I read a directive, printed on the family press. For a nonmemory, I have worried that one quite a lot. And the only proof, the photograph, is missing.

When I was fourteen I won a statewide essay contest. I wrote about the American Indian, his plight, his prospects. I recall an overuse of the word 'vivid': sunset over the reservation, Indian skin, eyes, imagery (some examples of this taken from the life), an adjective in fact for everything except his prospects, and I trusted that the words of my plea to change his prospects from dreary to vivid were as vivid as I thought.

I wrote about Indians because I was closely associated with one, an artificial cousin, an unadopted son of an aunt with whom I spent the summers. Everything about him was vivid, from the rectal pain he caused me (until I was ten years old, at which age it mysteriously did not hurt anymore, but I had five good years of vivid rectal pain) to the words he used to teach me about nature. He was nineteen, smooth as sweet oil, his rough black hair like a flower, a peony, my aunt said. Together we sought the nests of setting hens in haymows, rode animals, even cows, in bareback, sometimes nude, raffishness, swam, caught catfish with our hands and routed out of muddy ponds creatures not always recognizable, that lumped upon the land like heaving exposed brains, their efforts at locomotion as weighty as thoughts of aloneness. These nameless animals gave to my earliest thinking a respect for the subterranean.

Because of my Indian, I learned that what is ethical need not be moral, may, indeed, be its opposite.

I have spoken of the pain caused me not to gain sympathy, which increases pain and is addictive, but in an effort to make connection between the latest nonmemory—my fragments of poesy —and that first excruciating reality. If I can make connection only once between the real and the non then I believe the haunting could subside, and even that I could understand the nonexistence of records of myself when young. I cannot make the sought connection clearer to you until it is clearer to me, which clarity may dawn when I have made a connection, however slight.

I should interject here the fragments of poetry ('poetry'), the result of nonmemory, for they seem to point the way to an ethical suicide. Everything, it seems by the fragments, can trust itself to wake up tomorrow except the 'I':

> The podded mimosa rattling like a sistrum
> Can point to its healed wound and think Spring;
> The buoy in the Creek, through water lightening
> To ice, can feel the tug of the anchor
> And understand that freeze leads to thaw
> And thaw to sails again;
> Elsewhere and all about, expectancy:

And here occurs the curious line already given:

> The grass browning toward sleep
> Like a child met halfway
> By his dream of fur

Everything, it seems, except the 'I' of the poem has reason to go on, and as the poem's I is the I of this biography, artifact or not, and expresses well enough the doubts of a lifetime for me, there is a certain urgency in the circling and search, though my personal desire for continuity is, as it has been for some time, mainly literary.

Perhaps digression is only an acted-upon need for respite, a mask for deep reluctance to unearth the kernels of one's behavioral life. Because of my Indian, I learned that what is ethical need not be moral, may be its opposite, and though I believe it, I glimpsed when I first set the words down a twisting thread setting the pattern for later distortions.

Whether or not at the age of five or six I knew the difference between moral and immoral can't be important. I had learned that it was wrong to hurt someone, particularly someone younger and smaller than you, and I knew from experience that the result was punishment. Thus when I was hurt, was being hurt, and my aunt came into the room having heard a sound, so she said, I—still connected under the covers to my source of pain—had to decide if my pain outweighed his punishment. What he was doing was wrong because it hurt me, but what my confession would do would be still more wrong: I had already been hurt, but he was unscathed; to confess would mean that he would be hurt, and I knew without complications of thought that his punishment would be severe, even horrible. If I knew it because I wished it, which is one path to both learning and invention, I cannot recall. I loved him in the daytime and knew that he loved me at night with a different kind of pleasure, and I could not have him punished for taking his pleasure.

In the scene my aunt is a voice, and while he talked to her reassuring her, she is the sound of breathing. I do not know why her breaths are so loud in my memory. There is no light in the memory, though she may have carried one. If the remembered darkness was pain, or thought, or willful blindness, or because I was buried beneath him, I cannot say. There is no transition. I see us next as viewed through binoculars, two figures far up a road like a riverbed between high banks. It may recently have rained; there is no dust to mark our passage.

Does the foregoing sag in the middle because it is weighted with lies? Are lies then heavy and truth buoyant? Is it anthropopathy to invest abstractions with physical properties?

Interesting to speculate that if truth is an abstraction and its natural twin a lie, then a lie is as well an abstraction, which would seem to put it out of harm's way. And yet it is much easier to recognize a lie than it is to know a truth on sight. A person possessed of his faculties may, for example, say, "I am dead," and the statement is plainly a lie. But if some people say "I am alive," so many qualifications come into being that we must (even if the person is ourself) give it up as unprovable.

The story does sag in the last section, and I believe this is so because it is crammed with lies. I did not call out to my aunt because I was petrified with embarrassment and was, and knew it by then, a coward. I knew that what was happening was wrong, but it was my own guilt that concerned me. I was not then, nor ever have been, concerned with morals or ethics. In adulthood I have excused myself on the grounds of membership in that ever-spreading and increasingly undefinable group called artists. In childhood, if I was good, it was because I feared punishment; if I was bad, it was because I believed I could get away with it. The eye of God concerned me sometimes, but far from persistently; it was an unpleasantly stalky thing (not unlike my 'mind's eye') poking through clouds and lavatory walls, mainly when I was masturbating. Once it resolved itself into the eye of my real father, but because punishment did not follow, I never again suffered guilt over the practice.

Hap was masturbating when I killed him. As a sensual aid he was employing a bar of soap, which he worked into a lather by spitting copiously on it, great fresh young globs of shining saliva. It was a bar of Bloomingdale's lanolin Carnation, deeply scented, monogrammed with the store's elegant 'B'. He used so much salivaed soap in his long futile labor over himself that when I noticed it again it was to see that the 'B' had been worn away.

Why, one may ask, leave the lie-weighted section in the story if it merely sags? especially the premature nobility (if that mode of behavior is ever anything but); at the I's denial of a quest for sympathy·through tales of pain one imagines the reader's mouth set in a grin, recalling that a young thing is like Blanche DuBois: he must rely on the kindness of strangers in a world composed of strangers. The child as well as the puppy must waggle and beg for sympathy because the other side of sympathy is something that maims.

I leave the section there because I think that in its willful distortion, in the invention of quite another life and experience, may be discerned the seed, or what comes before the seed, of those hauntings I refer to as nonmemories.

My prize-winning essay, with its overuse of 'vivid,' replaced the Indian in my life. I had been replaced by a child named Burn, a Fresh Air Kid who came to breathe and stayed to usurp. His name, according to my aunt, meant 'stream' in Scots. I thought it meant exactly what it said, and the mark it left was vivid. My essay was filled with good intentions fully realized, through my artistry; with distillations that left only the Indian's nobility; with lies which became official and thus 'the truth.' My essay, a nonmemory, became a memory. Only now—and to whom?—do I confess my authorship of lies.

## II

My attempt to assay the year with Low* (my attempt to 'to attempt,' in the English that formed me) may have had a root similar to my Indian essay: to analyze pain as though it were a friend, a lover; to find the familiar that lives in all strangeness; finally, to put that pain, that strangeness, in the favored position usually accorded ourselves; to give it precedence over us, physically, morally; or—if that is mentally impossible, as it is for me—then to incorporate it into ourselves so that the Indianness, the birthmark, are, too, our own distinguishing marks.

The distillation of Low that I gave permanent form—the eliding of all his quirks and dishonesties, the romanticizing of his psychopathy—were even more serious a misuse of my abilities than the reduction of my complex Indian to a single-strand nobility. At least that maiden voyage was to escape a country in which my life was imperiled. By the time I met Low, I had made so many such voyages to and from so many countries that my gesture, for him, was mere hedonism: to don his birthmark as though it were a costume for a fancy dress ball. A Mod gesture, in this age of deliberate hideousness.

In the first person, one can own up to anything, one's candor being the balm to the wound of shock: I say this about MYSELF, forgive me!—a direct appeal, nearly always granted, with the great example of *mea culpa* the pedestal on which most Western religions rest. But in the third person even one's own person, the *allos ego*, if monstrous, is held against the author.

Thus I say here, as I could not in the story "The Birthmark," that I was constantly repelled by that constellation, that Andromeda of an affliction. It was as though my bride had brought the serpent along, twining breast and back and thigh, the tail resting just above the instep. When Low, and I, Perseus, sat thigh to thigh in the evenings listening to music, and his leg, crossed over the other at the knee, bounced to the beat, I would gaze in a trance of dismay at his trouser-cuff above the bare foot, waiting for the music to enliven the snake and cause it to stretch so that its tail could be seen. At such times, when the motion of the bouncing foot hiked the cuff up and displayed the birthmark at the instep, if I was sitting with my arm about his shoulders as he liked it to be, I would imagine that I could feel the serpent's flattened head

---

* The author refers here to "The Birthmark," included in *New Directions in Prose & Poetry 27.*—Editor

lifting on Low's back. An effort of great will kept my arm there, forced it to press harder and harder to kill the snake beneath the shirt, which Low would take as urgent sexual need. Revulsion can be an aphrodisiac, too, as I learned that year with Low.

Hap's chest was a mass of scars, healed in ropes of exposed and twisted muscles. One thigh, from groin to knee on the inside, was made up of a piece of flesh different in color and texture, hairless; it was like a piece of lamb fell, or a snake's shed skin. His tongue was cleft! These wounds were the result of a fall of one hundred fifty feet in a canyon. In the fall a memory bank had been wiped out. Hap spoke haltingly when formulating sentences, but when he referred to the loss of a memory bank the technical terms he had learned came pouring forth as though from the groove in a record. At times his tongue lolled, fat and forked, from the corner of his curly mouth. The sensation of placing the tip of my tongue in the groove of his was like (rather than causing) *déjà vu;* it was like a waking dream of bestiality. Once he crouched on the floor tongue-touching with my dachshund. I spoke to him sharply. It seemed to me that her excitement in the game was unnatural. (It was later that he spoke of mounting her, tried to penetrate her with his finger—fatal move.)

By equating, however ineptly, Hap with Low, I am trying to do one of two things, or so it occurred to me in the break represented above by space which represents another telephone call, this time to a phone said not to be 'a working number,' all evidence of Hap now faded or fading:

1. To give Hap the spurious substance I have given Low, which is to make him more literary than not, a metaphor;

2. To put Low in Hap's position, which may be: murdered by me, the snake successfully slain and belly up at last.

In that phrase 'belly up at last' rests another possibility, a purely sexual wish, one, if a wish, unrealized with Low, and I might add with Hap. Both had severely afflicted thighs, the blisters of Low's matched by the parchment deadness, paper brittleness, of Hap's, so that to have placed the face in that vicinity would have been unaesthetic. Hap tried to force my head there; Low, when naked, covered himself there with cupped hands like a parody of a virgin. The two impulses are aligned, at this moment overlapping. Just so are Low's passivity to buggery and Hap's fighting rejection of it and effort to become the buggerer curiously superimposed, a perfect fit with no edges to be trimmed with a scissors. Between these two transparent layers I can see myself pressed, the three of us lined up for a photograph which when developed depicts only one—but one what? Urge? (Photographable nowadays in the offices of neurologists and in courtrooms.) Thumbprint?—the thief and liar, the hustler, the criminal lobotomized by nature (Hap was running from Justice, seventeen-year-old fugitive, among Colorado labyrinths) revealed as one? If so, I state in some excitement (literary) that the nonmemories are essentials, fillers for the missing memory bank, and for Low's dread that his birthmark, too, was missing. In unconsciously choosing 'photograph' as a condition by which the three of us are revealed to be one, I have finally made a connection with myself, with my own perhaps only important loss, the photograph of me as a child.

In its place, I am astounded to consider, I have so far without regret, remorse, or actual recall, been pleased enough to put a squeamish murderer. Is anything, then, better than nothing? Or just how important to the sake of identity are tangible records? Vagrants, without geographical or provable familial associations, regularly confess to crimes that they did not commit; some die for crimes which are surely nonmemories. Sometimes, as recently in the case of Whitmore, or Whitimore, justice—however, by default —prevails and they are set free, but it was the black's nonmemory that won him several years behind bars. 'Won'—*le mot juste;* it was a prize avidly sought. If I succeed in convicting myself here, my own words will be my jail, which will be no change at all in the *status quo.*

As every corridor and chinkhole must be assayed, are these nonmemories then my effort to break out of my word-jail? Listing in the order of their importance to me, if I could amass—invent: enough colors, primary or dilute; strains of melody; artifacts singular either because unflawed or monstrously flawed; some people—food producers and sex providers, mainly; and finally a series of psychological moments like bursts of fireworks—all these to furnish and make acceptable a small flat tapestrylike world, I would step into it with no backward glance at a world which for too long has been 8½ x 11 inches. This world I have peopled with the spectrum of human aberration, but its grisaille renders it jejune. The effect is prevailing weariness pierced only by need which, when satisfied, produces more weariness.

Pride too often litters the path of understanding like a rockfall, a *Steinschlag,* but weariness, temporary defeat—especially—can be

heavy enough machinery to push the rocks aside, and in relief at
having been spared mortal concussion I can acknowledge the bond.
I now fully accept that Hap's loss of a memory bank is linked however mysteriously to the loss of my photograph. For a moment I am
even able to believe that Hap and I are—were—the same person.
But if his murder is only a kind of literary suicide, I am still caught
in velleity.

I was brought up on the following quote from F. Scott Fitz-
gerald: "The best people are always hard on themselves." At some
point in my education I came upon those words in *Tender Is the
Night* and was astounded by their context: Nicole's sister had
danced until two A.M. with an icebag strapped to her side under
her evening dress, was operated on at seven the next morning for
appendicitis. The reason for her masochism was that she had *three
royal princes on her dance card*. Therefore (?), the lesson I was
meant to learn was: the best people are snobs.

Among the creative acts of my time—how desperately I worked
to avoid the quotes around creative; such mental endeavor, the
mind pushing against itself, must fall in the category of isometric—
we have witnessed one painter erasing the work of another, possibly
greater painter. As snobbism is an ultimate reduction, perhaps the
ultimate reduction to its lees of ego, then this act is one of basest
snobbishness. Destructiveness in art—self-destructive machines, self-
defeating artists—has become a fixture of what I will again refer to
as my time, though to claim this time as my own is another destruc-
tive gesture, in the sense of my contribution to it and its influence
upon me. Surely a person, even a thalidomide baby, is the result of
creative endeavor, therefore an Art object. In my extreme snobbism
I have—may have—joined the Movement by destroying Hap. We
are said to be made in the image of our creator(s). Hap's beauty
could have led one to believe in a radiant God, his flaws only the
reversal of coloration and texture that one finds on a photographic
negative. I should like to have seen the negative of my baby photograph. More than that, I should have liked to have sensed its oppo-
siteness, the reversal of values: little thief become little saint, for
instance. The projection into the future of those negative values
would, of course, have turned little pervert into Little Mister Normal. At this juncture, to become my own opposite is the only way
I can visualize for myself salvation. My dimensions, when cubed,
enclose me in a prison of self. The clear plastic walls stop me from
further outward movement, though I may stand at the barriers and

see beyond them the paths that I may have taken stretching to, for me, impossible horizons. I see my projections trudging, leaping, advancing with dignity, flying, burrowing, while I, fossil in amber, maintain—maintained—illusions of freedom: of movement, of choice, of thoughts, the three fates from whose loins issue the whole of life.

One longs for acceleration, longs to have done with the Jamesian equivocations, the parenthetical clauses, the ifs, ands, perhaps, buts. The desire to *make connection* is as acute as sexual need, if sexual connection permanently altered one's state; as it is, my body tautens to receive that first alien touch, my mind dilates to receive the images that sustained will finally push me into the climax and beyond, into a kind of peace. For as in the aftermath of sex there is no escape from knowledge that aberration was achieved, and so one is forced to *make one's peace,* so I long for the No Exit of the past tense: I DID, I WAS, and therefore I AM.

I dream serenely. In my dreams all is contained within the past. When I walk in a dream it is down a road traveled long ago. Figures of the past crowd my dreams, even though I know that I have never seen them before. Nonmemories such as those never-seen figures cast no cloudy projections on the road before me. My world is contained, so that a densely tree'd country road affords glimpses of deep chairs, sofas, marble pools with heated towels nearby. Even the rain falls from the roof of my contained world, my house. A dusty mill beside a bleak river is part of the furniture; a pasture gate leads into a carnival area, one of whose rides is eternity, so that my house contains achieved death. All the people I have known in life stand below looking up toward the cockpit in which I and my dachshund ride forever. In my dreams I have made connection with everything, and the peace of the No Exit of the past tense settles constantly over me like clouds of yeast spores borne to an arbor of grapes. Like ripeness, the past is immanent.

## III

I think I have not confused these nonmemories with the inventions I call stories, which are nearly innocent of events. I can imagine that a writer with a 'tapestry' of characters, foreground and background carefully woven, might in some late remembrance recall his inventions as having had real flesh and blood. I am a dealer in words only: I am confined, not always willingly in the past, to the belief that the sole movement in my stories may be only the motion a word may have. When I write 'he ran' I see neither him nor running; I see two words. In the stories of others, a handful, sunlight 'lights,' flowers 'bloom,' sometimes a 'house' has rooms, verandas, history. Thus some of these others have 'gifts' for writing, while I construct sentences which have 'grace,' for instance, only if they contain the word 'grace.' In some lexicon with private application to me, a 'graceful' writer is one who uses the word 'grace' to excess.

This limitation, imposed upon me (I see it this way: $\frac{limitation,}{me}$ allowing the line, in a reckless mood, to represent 'upon') could be either from skepticism or fear. I acknowledge that spoken or written sentences can hurt even when they do not contain the word 'hurt'; therefore they must be able to kill—or so this theory could, if allowed, run.

But nowhere does this digression bring me closer to an answer (compulsively, I set down here that the only way, in my terms, that 'me' can be brought closer to 'an answer' is to move it there, as in 'give me an answer,' the imperative move resulting, not surprisingly, in an imperative), unless by denial I have managed to remove a fragment of some barrier (which in my increasing compulsion is accomplished by removing 'fragment' from the sentence, which, anyhow, was not a part of 'some barrier'). Removing fragments, in the sense of letters, from 'some barrier' would be to acknowledge the existence of an actual barrier within the words, with the letters seen as stonelike fragments, and though I can discuss it, I cannot see it, and so the action would be foolish.

In this sort of indulgence the only activity comes to lie entombed within parentheses; words and I are divorced from each other, and the game is between the typewriter—instrument of removal—and the self-erected barriers of parentheses, which, unlike the words 'some barrier,' do resemble fences; so that finally the page is filled with (     ) (     ) (     ); then the pages, then the book. A new art form, like Rauschenberg erasing De Kooning? Or madness? No, it is only page, pages, book, filled with parentheses, lines, marks, ('s. Finally one learns to leave the paper as it was found, unmarked; and then one does not bother to find it.

Among my compulsions is counting, which someone said was calculated to take the place of thought, and though I said that thought was required to count—mainly any parallel lines, or sets of symmetrical figures—stair risers, or squares in wallpaper, or windowpanes—really I lied because it had become so automatic that it was not counting but a sort of assessment by intuition: a sweeping glance across a newly encountered window, and one is somehow emotionally informed of something which the nerves, probably, register. Balance, it seems, becomes the object: one is either reassured or disquieted by the sense of proportion—or angered, or, as has happened, sexually aroused. There were rooms in the world that I could walk into and relax with, the relaxation the result of old neural assessment, though these rooms were very rare. Usually my nerves armed themselves at thresholds against the emotional horrors of architectural imbalance. There were no new books, for example, no matter the publicity, that I could open without that forearming, and very few old ones. The dictionary, which 'contains' 'emotion,' but also has 'none,' was safest for me in certain moods; though the Random House one here was so full of errors that it contained emotion in quite another sense.

This is how I see the personal part of that sentence: 'was' 'safest' 'for' 'me' etc. In other words, there is 'safety' but there is no safety.

'I' 'must' 'stop' 'this.' How do 'I' 'stop' 'this'? Obviously, 'I' cannot, but the typewriter can erase it, thus:

'I' 'must' 'stop' '         .'
            and
'I' 'must' '         .'
            and
'I' '         '
            and
'I'
            and
'   '

Murder by subtraction.

But then one comes to rely solely upon punctuation, otherwise the murder would be unnoticed. . . For a moment, such is the nature of hope that has led one to write in the first place (to write 'in the first place'!), there is a little upspringing of belief that such a story might be 'written,' composed entirely of punctuation. One thinks of it as the ultimate (up to now, though someone is undoubtedly working on it) collaboration between author and reader, for though supplying punctuation, the author does not dictate whether, for example, ! is to indicate surprise, joy, anger, emphaticness, command or plea, among other possibilities. ? may seek knowledge, or confirmation of what one already knows, or may merely take the place of such a sentence as "He waited politely, eyebrows raised, for her to continue." In music there is a kind of composition which gives options, of melody, rhythm, key, to the performer. In such a book as mine, 'serial' would acquire an entirely new meaning: title, *The Serial Songbook.*

As the typewriter easily eliminates 'I,' so does my new method eliminate the idea ('I' dea) of author, or rather, Author. He now could fuse with typesetter, who drunkenly has been his collaborator since the invention of type. Thus, vanishing, the Author gives sanction to the murder of words.

Or, choice still persisting like some vestigial organ, one arrives back at the blank page which one may now fill with words, this time punctuationless. And so it goes     the seesaw     *le mot juste*     for the choice is finally confined     as it was in the beginning     to stasis and illusion     static on the ground     illusion of flight on the brief surge     and so it reduces to emotion     mood up     mood down. (Finality must retain its mark willy nil.) To obtain evenness on the seesaw     the device functionless then     is to stand     you and opponent     without moving the plank between the legs.

Finally, you will notice how hopefully I have used 'finally,' as though the cluster of letters held within them the mysterious ability to draw to a conclusion the events defined by the words that follow the word 'finally.' Finally, one has reduced oneself to words that contain no movement or possibility of movement, so that one also is without the capability of movement. 'Murder,' then—surely?—defines only itself, which is to say, its parts: m,u,r,d,e,r. The only possible movement, action, surrounding the word is of accumulation, a letter at a time, and this accomplished, it lies upon the page, harmless, erasable.

Erasable, yes; harmless, no. As words have histories of associations, they have futures that may contain influences exerted. There is a great terror, in putting down words, that the influence, in some future time, may be a bad one. That the words may maim, depress, lead to acts the reverse of what one thought one meant. Hate on a page intended for the printer must be carefully so carefully! put in perspective so that for the reader there is no possible confusion that might let him see hate as a directive. Thus moral conclusions must be drawn, or clearly implied; the artist is never freed from this obligation. Never. Every word written swims before my eyes in this curious drowning death stripped of camouflage. I see, knowing that the reader has seen, the deadly directive posing as satire;

the racial epithet no longer hiding behind compassionate usage, the prurience kerneled within the 'liberated' scene: nothing is more painfully pornographic than sex described by a Christian in whom natural lasciviousness is endlessly being punished by a puritan up-bringing, a kind of ageless schoolmarm whose birches are ones very own roots. . . Simile, metaphor, corrode from the acid of sudden vision and flake away, and the supportive rod, brutish weapon, stands alone.

*2 a.m.*

Some crisis is imminent, or immanent, for though I go about among my fellows, in crisis acknowledging kinship—explosive, mur-derous, with a raging, joyless sexuality—no ray escapes to burn them or give them warning. In the Post Office I 'accidentally' brush another's flesh with mine, expecting recoil but am smiled upon; apologies are murmured. Only Miss Gold, tonight, shifted away from me, putting space between us. When I awoke a while ago I found her on the opposite side of the bed barely within arm's reach. When I touched her, her muzzle trembled, infinitesimally hitched upward like an Austrian blind, revealing her teeth. She has not done this since the fierce long abandoned games of puppyhood. I feel as though she is telling me that she now requires notice so that she may prepare herself for my caress.

*p.m.*

I walked with my feet in the cold Atlantic and wept; wept be-cause I had not swum there this past summer; wept for Miss Gold's beauty as she stretched her neck, sniffing the salt, a dachshund dreaming of swans; wept for our masquerade, ineffective and soon over, for it seemed to me a time of summing up and casting aside. The quiet water encroached in the guise of other, new continents, self-stenciled on this old one, that I felt I would be leaving, desti-nation unknown. But not as a stranger; no longer as a stranger. I and my companion will no longer hide within the skins of Chris and Miss Gold. Like island hoppers, we have leaped from life to life, discovering in the spaces between that crucifixion has many forms, that self-crucifixion is the most unpardonable sin; that I stand guilty before my self, which may be, before God.

# FOUR POEMS

MICHAEL McCLURE

## WRITTEN IN EDINBURGH

PEOPLE ARE LIKE STARS
BUT THEY
are more
hot.
Their swelling patterns
divide all space
between them
and
they
colonize
new dimensions.
(Our numbers
make actions
meaningless.
Territory
becomes a mental
rigor.)
In the Highlands
is pink-green moss—
one's hand can
enter it to the wrist.
A shepherd's life is beautiful.

# LINES WITH WHITEHEAD*

"The penetration of intuition follows upon
the expectation of thought."
The flatworm dimly lights his cave.
The mastodon tramples
on the brilliant tundra.
We feel in waves
and ride upon them
like silver surfers
coasting
through
the
nave.
"This is the secret
of attention."

---

Our skin is taught
by moving torches
making loops.
Wrists have wings.
The eagle sings
with screeches.

# WINDOW

THAT IS THE GORGEOUSNESS
OF MY SUNSET
over the island of trees
in blue mist.
The pink, pale purple,
and mauve are me
hurrying to be free
and calling
THE BLACK
to be
a bed for the bevy
of billions

* Quotes are from A. N. Whitehead, *The Function of Reason,* Princeton University Press, 1929.

of starlets
that streak
forever
outward
to peek
at my brow
that faces
the setting sun.

---

I
am the center,
the flame,
the delicate saraband
of the elves!

# A THOUGHT

IS THE INSTANT SO COMPLEX?
CAN WE EXIST?
Like Fausts can we be the fist
of ourselves
or are we tiny flowers
floating on the mass of blossoms
drifting
on
the
edge
of thunderstorms?
We are shapes
*unique*
not forms.
We are wolves
(not possums
drooling
rolling
in the dust);
we lope into the darkest
forest.
Any particle of time
is just enough!

# EIGHT POEMS

ARTUR LUNDKVIST

*Translated by W. H. Auden with Leif Sjöberg*

TRANSLATORS' NOTE: *Artur Lundkvist, born in 1906, makes his home in Solna, outside Stockholm. A giant in Swedish poetry, he has also written novels, short stories, and essays; his recent* Lustgårdens demoni *(Bonniers, 1973), the title of which refers to Hieronymus Bosch, was his sixtieth book. Lundkvist has always kept in close touch with modern literary developments and world trends. In 1927 he translated poems by Edgar Lee Masters and Carl Sandburg, while the following year his first volume of poems,* Glöd *("Glowing Embers"), showed a marked influence by Walt Whitman, among others. In the essay collections* Atlandvind *("Ocean Wind," 1932) and* Ikarus flykt *("The Flights of Icarus," 1939), Lundkvist wrote on Surrealism and such authors as Sandburg, Whitman, Sherwood Anderson, Eugene O'Neill, Thomas Wolfe, John Dos Passos, James Joyce, William Faulkner, Henry Miller, and Saint-John Perse. Tirelessly he has introduced contemporary authors to his countrymen: Patrick White was just one writer he spotted years before anyone else. Lundkvist's own work has been translated into several languages, although there is as yet no collection of his in English.*

## THE ROCKS

The rocks are drowning in the rising sea,
the lighthouse-keeper's red cottage is carried away,
together with the fishing nets,
the lighthouse is lit up at the last moment
and its ray is drowned in the depths,
the piers are dissolved like chalk in water,
the echo flees from the drowning grottoes,
the fir trees stretch their burning arms towards the sky,
but the soft green advances upwards towards the mountaintop,
like when a wading woman lifts her skirt.

## THE ANTS

are busy conquering the earth.
The soil sinks under the foot
that tramples on ant-tunnels and is immediately attacked.
The ants hollow out walls so that the houses collapse.
They crowd into lamps so that the light is extinguished.
They creep into the orifices of the human body
and ravage them like black fire.
They peer out of portraits through the eyes they have eaten.
They let themselves drop from branches into breast orifices
so that the horses bolt.
In the morning they have settled in shoes
and can only be driven out by powerful jets of water.
They force their way into safes and devour valuable papers.
They attack printing offices and replace the type with ants.
They overrun rails so that the trains are derailed.
They invade cities till bomb shelters are no longer any use.
There is no protection against the ant hordes
and nowhere to escape from them.
They die in billions but never feel defeated.
They are more effective than blowtorches.
They grow with their task,
become bigger and more irresistible every day,
armour-clad and armour-eyed.

They continue to attack even after their bodies have been
    half crushed.
They eat rubber like bread,
drink milk and whiskey without discrimination.
They are as relentless as ice and fire combined.
They triumph over everything
without, perhaps, being even aware of their power.


## MAYAKOVSKY

often sat on the bench beneath the rowan tree
as the summer day grew cooler over Moscow.
He put clusters of rowan berries into drinking glasses
before the wind came with snow from Siberia.
He, a poet?
No, a horseman, a foot with long strides.
A lumberjack among fir trees falling like brothers.
A smith among sparks that lit up the night.
A barefoot ploughman on a stubble-ground of iron.
A voice that thundered over the heads of the crowd
at railway stations where the rain wept through leaking roofs.
A head of steel and eggshell
in the deafening din from hammers and anvils.
He: a poem in top boots, on the march
through the mud, through the snow,
through rubbish heaps and deserted palaces:
a poem with a kitten in its breast pocket,
displaying a tongue like a lead on a briar rose.
And the girl with braids hanging over her breasts
came with apples, wet from the October trees,
the women in waders and drenched coats
with breasts steaming as they came indoors.
The accordion player sat on the pile of lumber
as the river shone like a fish between dirty dykes.
Crowds, singing on the march,
flour spilled on the ground,
rinds of cold bacon in the hand.
A layer of snow on a slice of coarse bread,

a poem stained with indelible ink
And, suddenly, an exhaustion
that opened the door
to another passion, that burst forth wildly.
A foot in the crevice between two rocks.
a cluster of rowan berries in the snow.


## THE MAGPIE

The bird of my breezy humor
flies whirling like a helicopter
a sphere of wings on the wind.
The magpie, merry widow laughing,
despite her neglected children, laughing
at thefts she has committed and intends to commit.
Black-white bird of birches
at home even in trees that stand out black against the snow.
Autumn's rowan berry picker without a basket
her breast steel-shimmering like a cold clear winter sky.
But she loves the farmyards better than the forests
flying through chimney smoke that smells of frying bacon,
picks up a safety pin that was thrown out with the baby's
        bath water,
and, sitting on a wooden pump, listens to the cream separator in
        the kitchen.
The magpie, artful girl with waggling tail
never really young and inexperienced,
more like a gypsy with a silver coin in her ear
easily seduced in the last hay remaining over from
        the spring-winter,
when feet are cold from rain.
But never either a peevish hag like the crow,
nor hoarse like the raven, that wandering horse dealer,
with a knife under his coat and a quid of tobacco in his trap.
No, most closely related to the poor parson's spinster daughter
who dances on the ice
in spite of her tattered mittens.
The magpie with a bundle of sticks and a squeaking milk can,

dressed in blown-away egg-white, dipped in tar from drainpipes,
dwelling in the weather-proofed wooden houses, in a land
where she sharpens her beak on the grindstone,
and laughs her contempt for boys who climb trees.


## MORE THAN ENOUGH

of truths with severed feet
and news with a handkerchief in its mouth.
More than enough
of quotation marks around reality,
of clergy who nail up doors
and youths who go to bed with bicycles,
of love's uninhabited nesting-boxes,
of scars from burns that are seeking knife edges,
of family life's pickled herring
and theatres facing royal stables.
More than enough
of swans who have outlived their castles,
of needles that suddenly protrude from thighs,
of brides who have been blinded by crossed corkscrews,
of horses that kick in the door
in order to deliver some meaningless printed matter.
Yes, more than enough, more than enough
of babies within bodies weighing a hundred kilos or more,
of tankers decorated with white asters,
of stars that never fall
and stars that are always falling,
of dogs inside houses and blazing hearths without fires,
of hair-partings in the nape of the neck and centipedes in
        the ear,
of winter flies and hiccups and heels worn down on one side,
and horsehair sticking out of the collar of a jacket.
More than enough, more than enough, more than enough
of all the false, the futile, the outdated,
and never enough of the necessary, the essential
that is more than half alive.

# FROM OTHERS YOU TAKE WHAT YOU DON'T WANT

From others you take what you don't want
    but don't hesitate in front of that which you most desire.
If you meet someone else, you remain strangers
    who have looked for the same ford.
You rent your room from the randy mother
    with the frigid daughter: a turnstile of errors.
On rainy days sullen bees get caught in your hair.
    On other days you observe how a thrown stone
    leaves a faint trace in the air.
You possess no land of your own, no tree, not a single one,
    nor a well: instead you intensify
    your proprietary right to the world.
In dreams at times you drown bees in a river,
    but your hatred of others is nothing
    but your hatred of yourself.
Your idea of yourself is your everlasting tyrant.
    Freedom is given you merely to cultivate
    and harvest yourself, a crop to distribute.
In stillness you imagine storms, and peace under the waves,
    see everywhere that which is not but only to come.
    That is why you are loved by few.

# THE HORSE

comes out of the forest, white like forgotten snow.
He comes out of the rye fields
and has a bleeding hoof.
He rises out of the well
with a wooden key in his mouth.
The horse is made of the river's froth and the current's force.
He paws beneath the trees and waits by the fire.
He gazes darkly out of his abundant blood,
and has lips as soft as the moss upon stones in the water.
He is the horse I am waiting for at the crossroads,
the horse who burns beneath me
and resembles a nude woman in the summer night.

The horse who bears me onwards over serpents and thistles,
who flies through windows and rears himself up against walls.
The horse with whom I roam beneath the clouds like a wing,
and ride straight through the haystacks, those aged
clouds on the ground.
Until he begins to sink ever deeper into the grass,
and disappears like water into the earth,
leaving me standing there motionless, without speed and
    carrying blood,
waiting for him to rise out of the earth once again,
out of the well or spring with a key in his mouth,
from a well frequented by ferns and woodpeckers,
with a key dripping water,
a horse who shines red beneath the white mist of his skin.


## A LOVE OF WOOD

calls for the sharpest steel, says the carpenter.
How wonderfully alive is Wood
under a shining steel-sharp axe!
How gentle the cuts through its rings
formed after the spring floods!
Inside Wood there ticks a clock
or perhaps a heart.
Wood is Time,
stratified like waves on a shore.
Wood contains more compressed Time
than Man,
that is why it is harder, more lasting.
Wood has a fragrance lovelier than the skin of a woman.
It sweats small fruits, small golden grapes.
It shows its sex in every branch,
male and female in one, both joined together,
and doubly hard under the axe.
Who can enter into Wood and survive?
But who does not wish that he could?
The dead are laid to rest in Wood like the unborn.
(Oh, to rest there in deepest sleep

like a cigar in a fragrant box!)
Beauty must be won from Wood,
lasting life also.
It does not die like Man, suddenly
a stinking corpse.
No, Wood is alive in death
more firmly and freshly than any flesh.
With tender hands
and the sharpest tools,
I shall finally penetrate Wood,
feel Wood in my mouth and throat,
feel Wood embrace me,
firmly, securely, for ever.

# FROM *FICTION AS LIFE STYLE*

WARREN JAY HECHT

## A LETTER TO THE CHIEF

Chief Grey Cloud August 6, 1971
c/o The Black Water Queen
The Black Cross River, Minnesota

Dear Chief:

I have nothing against you. I got your name off a billboard. I considered but decided the lady wouldn't let me come back, nailing them around the kitchen window in the cabin. The fishing was good, although as you can see only one pike. Maybe I was over anxious. They all came from this place where the bank widens into a crescent and the water is deeper and out of the sun most of the day. It said *reservations* after your name. I suppose you take people cruising on The Black Water Queen. I bet it's a paddle wheeler and you play the accordion. Sailing down the river on a Sunday afternoon. There's an Indian who does that in Ohio. My wife's mother took the trip and said he looked like an Hawaiian. You know, Mary and Beaver and Elaine and I got out of Beaver's Saab and headed across the street for the mall in Kalamazoo where, even though we didn't, we were given summonses for crossing against a *Don't Walk* sign and fined five dollars each—four for Michigan, one for Kalamazoo—twenty dollars. The cop kept saying he had nothing against me either. We had to pay because they'd suspend our driver's licenses if we didn't. The cop told me they can do it since it becomes resisting a warrant and refusing to appear on top of jaywalking. They may not like freaks and weirdos, Chief, but we went to the Kalamazoo County Fair, and if that's what they do like, forget it. One booth had hearts and lungs and stomachs and feet, even feet, and this little old lady who showed you the cancers on them and insisted I stop smoking and not drink coffee. She was a Seventh Day Adventist. Mary says that Kellodoublegood was one of them who was looking for a nonmeat food and invented corn flakes. Right opposite was another booth where they sit you down one on one and talk Jesus. When we went by they gave us a folder that said:

> Cool cat makes slick chick. WHAM—she's pregnant. He's a heel, she's an unwed mother. They're both losers in life's first inning.

I guess we looked loose. Well, Chief, I wanted to send these fish heads to someone and you're it. Remember, I have nothing against you. I might come up and ride your boat some time. You won't know it's me, but I'll know it's you. Have a good day.

Eddie

## YIELDING TO PARENTAL PRESSURE FRED VISITS TO MAKE HIS AUNT FEEL BETTER

Ralph the Dog, only one of many Ralphs simultaneously including Ralph, the Other Ralph, and The Breath of Life, greeted me at the fifth-floor double doors this afternoon disguised as Ralph, a college student and my father's sister's eldest son who, according to the frenzied sketches I'd received on returning from my New England sales push, deferred more and more to Ralph the Dog. He was dressed in a well-pressed though comfortable maroon embossed silk smoking jacket and cut quite a figure against the disheveled array dammed back by the orderly Mr. Ett. I asked, while stacking the fistful of dimes and nickels my aunt sent for soda and candy until Sunday when she came, how long Ralph the Dog had known my cousin, and was surprised to learn longer than believed although the principals themselves were hardly aware of the relationship till recently. The Other Ralph was indisposed. After a half hour of hinting I was forced to say outright I'd heard rumors of the elusive Breath of Life, reported tearfully to appear by my aunt and place all the Ralphs in a trance lasting irregular durations. How could The Breath of Life reduce Ralphs to a state like a coma? My cousin looked at me slowly, then smiled. "We," he said passing his left leg over the table between us, "do get tired."

## PROFESSOR BALFOUR'S BONDAGE

If I were not an honest man I'd deny the simple beauty of a broken heart. The Siamese attachment of joy to sorrow, this my wife and the police little understood, though Chelsea, despite her detachment from all emotion save sensual anticipation, sees the wet rose trellised round the bitter yew, the heavenly morning glory's blue lips open to the black locust's bunched thorns.

What is realized beyond the necessity of adjustment? Every situation, each star is a vicarious perception, the crazy collision of our minds and a cold, trigonometric light that fixes where we certainly are not. The unalterable sum of any triangle, the objective graph of any life only maps a straight line nailed rigidly to the self-determining iron grid of accidental intersection.

The image of Anne hung against the shower tiles like a seasoning deer arouses grief because death is not easeful, not a promised dream. I crouched on the chill black and white floor considering water seep between her stiff legs, imagining that final blank contraction, the blunt penetration into frozen clarity.

Did Anne foresee her insistence that my "creeping conservatism" was a "grey vine strangling our marriage" would lead to her erotic, acrobatic death? As I caressed the bloodwater down her child's breasts, fuller, more erect in inverted passion than ever in love, as wine channeled around her nipples, over her distended lips and dropped purple tears from her cheeks rouged with hard ecstasy, grand peace richened in me like honey.

Could Chelsea really return to her rectangular apartment, sweep the crescent shavings and bleached chips onto bleak Second Avenue, then settle into sleep's smooth nest? Or did she smear her body and mind with the same numbing aphrodisiac that impelled me to her and anticipate in retrospect the intricate weaving of hot leather, the shudder of the first splintering stab, the abandoned, disciplined twitching after Anne's damp consciousness evaporated into sharp icicles? I see this clearer than the slit moon through these flatly meshed bars.

What comes more naturally to man than love of simple beauty? Vast emotion reduces to a plain geometry, linear segments angled chaotically in translucence. While Chelsea rubbed white, anesthetizing crystals into Anne's sex, a colt's soft mouth forced open by the bit knotted between Anne's knees, while she slid the delicately carved staff slowly, gently, like an aged pump sucking black liquid long cooled in the blue heart of the sea, then faster, as my wife screams into the tasteless gauze, strains the thongs till the shower head wrenched from the wall, as I pressed my warm thumbs under her thrusting eyes I knew, in the calm of meditation, the rising circle, that Chelsea must remain free.

I am content. Her gift inscribes my spirit in the cloudless sphere, a hummingbird, the stillness of peonies.

## AROUND BATTLE CREEK

"No. We used to let men come up and hunt our field in November, but then the Van Horne's kid just missed getting hit." Jack's mother-in-law touched the hand-carved stock of an old pump-action .22 he found jammed inside a roll of chicken wire back in the tractor shed. She moved her hand across the stock. "No. All the neighbors agreed no more shooting." She rested her palm on the gun and tapped the barrel with her index finger. "When Ed died I hid it out there to keep it away from the kids." She lit a Pall Mall. "It's been out there nine years."

"Is it okay if I clean it up? I won't shoot it."

She knocked the ashes off the Pall Mall. "Ed didn't encourage guns. He bought this to keep the animals off the corn, but he never used it on anything besides cans."

Jack drove down to Houghtlin's and bought a kit and some steel wool for the barrel. The stock was scratched from the chicken wire.

He didn't know what to do with the stock, probably nothing, but it was a shame to mark up a hand-carved piece of wood. He worked on the gun in the kitchen while his mother-in-law made perogi. Gretchen was upstairs reading a history book.

"I wish you never found the gun."

Jack liked his mother-in-law. He considered her a novelty without realizing. "I won't shoot it." He rammed a piece of oil-soaked flannel down the bore. "I didn't buy shells."

"It always made me nervous when the kids were small . . ." She lowered a perogi into the boiling water gently on a spoon so the dough stayed intact around the mashed potatoes and cheese. ". . . to have a gun around the house." She stared at the gun. "Ed loved perogi. He said that's why he got along with my mother."

"Because of perogi?" He turned the instructions over.

"She made them for him all the time. It ain't easy."

Jack swung the gun up to the light and looked down the muzzle.

His mother-in-law skimmed the water with the spoon. "She made them with sauerkraut too. Ed loved her sauerkraut." She ran the spoon under the cold water. "He was real upset when Steiner told him to cut out sauerkraut."

The gun wouldn't pump. "Did she put up her own?"

"Sure. In five-gallon crocks. My Pa had to have sauerkraut. Don't cock that in the house."

"It's busted anyway." Jack leaned the rifle against the wall and took a cigarette from a pack of Pall Malls on the table. There were always two or three open packs of Pall Malls. He walked to the stove and leaned over the pot.

"One time a neighbor showed her how to put it up in jars and they exploded. All my Pa said was, 'Why did you have to go and mess with jars.' She wouldn't let him eat any of it because of glass."

"I can imagine," Jack said.

## THE HAIRY BUTTERFLY

"Oh yeah? Listen to this. You know Roy Leeds?"

"Sure."

"Well me and Roy and Larry Russ had the triple alliance back in high school. Roy just got a new Chevy when we was seniors and he was real careful about keeping it clean and all, so one day me and Larry said it's about time we broke it in and Roy says could be so we bought two cases of Coor's and headed up the coast. Next thing we're at Carpinteria. Man, I still don't know how we ended there or what happened on the way, but we took the last two sixes down to the beach.

"Me and Larry want to go swimming, but Roy says no cause we'll get all wet and sandy and mess the car, so we're sitting there when this guy and a chick come along and they got a fifth of rum with about this much left, so we traded a six pack for it and drunk it and all of a sudden Roy jumps up and runs into the ocean with me and Larry after him.

"When we got done we took off our clothes and put 'em in the trunk so we wouldn't wet the seats and got on the freeway and Larry's passing out in the back and I'm pretty sick so I says Roy stop the car or I'm gonna barf so he pulls over and we drag Larry out and lay him over the hood and he throws his guts up and I heave till I'm feeling better. Well I look around and I nearly died. Larry's still over the hood and Roy's standing there pissing straight up in the air and we're all stark naked only instead of pulling off to the right we're on the median with cars passing us both ways."

"Man."

"This still ain't over. Anyway, I drag Larry back in the car and get Roy and we take off again and make it to North Hollywood and Roy drops me at home. The next morning about eight I get this phone call from Roy's dad who's a steelworker from Illinois and he don't mince words. He says did Roy leave his car over at my house. I says I don't think so but let me check, but it's not there and I tell him to put Roy on but he don't remember nothing so I tell him I'll call Larry and be over in a couple minutes.

"Well we're sitting there trying to figure out where the car is when the phone rings and it's some guy in Bakersfield who says he's got Roy's wallet. Now man, that's over a hundred miles from where we was which confuses us more. Then about fifteen minutes later the state police call asking if he's the Roy Leeds who owns the Chevy. It turns out the car's driven right up against the front wall of some guy's house on a dead end halfway between Larry's place and Roy's. We went down there and it's sure the car, but reverse is gone. What we guessed is that Roy must of got lost on the way home and tried to make a U turn but blew reverse, so he locked the car and walked. And you know man, that's ten years ago and we still have no idea how his wallet ended up in Bakersfield or all the things we did that night."

"That reminds me of something when I was a freshman at Columbia. I was rushing my fraternity and the night before they gave out the bids they had a beatnik party and one of the brothers got me a date with his chick's best friend. I go to pick her up over on the West Side of Manhattan. Well, man, I get there and it's this super fancy old-time apartment house with doormen and chandeliers and the family has a maid. Well what was really a drag was this chick's dressed in a long gown and high heels to go to a beatnik party, right, so I say screw this and when we get up to the house I proceed to get stone drunk on Old Overholt rotgut. Well after the party the guy who got me the date drives us to take the girl home, only he's pissed at me because his chick's biting his ass since I got drunk so he throws me out of the car.

"The first thing I do is take a leak on the pole holding up the awning in front of her house and the doorman comes out to get me so I run around the corner and into the subway. And you got to remember I have no idea which train or nothing. Well, I decide I'm hungry and I got this pocket full of change so I buy about five or six ice cream sandwiches from a machine and I start throwing them at people across the tracks and screaming and yelling how they didn't have any sympathy for artists or something. I'm surprised I didn't get arrested. Anyway, a train comes and I get on and I'm riding around hollering when all of a sudden this guy grabs me and takes me upstairs to a cafeteria and gets me some coffee, then asks me where I lived and rides me back to my dorm in a cab and puts me to bed. You know I don't have any idea what he looked like except he was real tall and had a date."

"Strange."

"Yeah. I was lucky . . ."

"Well, it's after noon. If you still want to go through with this we better get going."

"I'm ready."

"You sure?"

"Sure. Just one more Coor's."

"What are you going to get?"

"I don't know. Maybe a moon or sun or something over here, but I got to see what the guy has. Man. I hope he's a salty old fucker with lots of tales to tell."

"Well let's go."

"How big does it look?"

"Pretty big. Man, I don't believe you did it."

"Oh man, how did it look when he was putting it on?"

"Bloody as shit. Man, I can't believe it."

"Fifteen bucks is cheap for something that big."

"Yeah, especially when you divide it over the rest of your life."

"What did you think of the one on his arm?"

"You mean the tiger and snake thing?"

"Yeah. Weird huh?"

"I don't know if you should talk."

"Nobody can see mine unless I show it to them."

"Well you better get a long swimsuit."

"The beach is cool."

"Does it hurt?"

"Not like when he was doing it. What's strange is having my leg shaved."

"When it grows back that's gonna be a hairy butterfly."

"Yeah."


## ROY COPS A RUSH

The fat wingspread pheasant flew five feet high, straight, iridescent, then dropped under the October corn and Roy wanted brushes, not the sucking, throaty tubes of the milking machine. He drove six feed-drooling cows out to the yard, emptied the six jars of milk into the dairy's closed, glass circulatory system, watched it spin and bubble to the stainless collecting tank and pulled the ropes letting six more beauties stroll into the stalls from the barn, cajoling them to stand still and eat their oats. God. It was like sleepwalking handling this machine, seven days, dawn and dusk, till he knew each Bessie or Lola or Dolores right down to the tip of her udders.

Was he stuck? When the old folks got sick, retired, or died their kids mostly sold, took the money and set up in some city where there were forty-hour jobs, work at honest, real pay, not the small change his brother raked out of the fields and he suctioned off the cows. He'd be better up at Ford's in Detroit, not twelve, sixteen hours a day out here. But there was the word they'd given Pa they'd keep the land in one piece and in the family, the promise he made in church two years ago Good Friday that he'd take no pride in painting till Jesus filled his talent with meaning. Yes, till Jesus led him away from the soil to do his work no subdivider would set up tin shacks on his father's land.

Roy looked out and saw a green dot consuming the brown corn, Jimmy on the tractor so far back in the fields he couldn't hear the engine, harvesting. Lucky Jim to work the land, watching the earth grow heavy with grain. But he had nothing else, no pictures in his head, nothing like painting. That's what Roy'd tried to say in Jimmy's portrait: Jimmy, strong, riding his combine over empty black, furrowed fields, reaping plowed ground before him, leaving ripe corn in his wake. Jimmy liked it enough, they hung it in the parlor, but when he came right down to it Roy knew his brother thought painting fools' play. The autumn fields and birds and the tractor's green reminded Roy of a picture by that Van Gogh. *His* brother was a big city art dealer.

Everyone in his graduating class talked about the cities, but as far as he knew only Rita Markley made it all the way to New York. Every time he saw her mom and she said how fine Rita was doing and told about those scholarships and auditions, Roy felt his cows kick him. If *he* could make it to New York and get a break, maybe paint one of those murals on a building or two like he saw in *Life Magazine*, then Rita would be glad enough to see him. They'd go around to museums with other painters and Rita'd introduce him to some of those show people and everything would be okay. He'd get him a motorcycle instead of a pickup and show her a fine old time.

Rita's grey skirt, like the one she wore in the senior play when he had to lift her around the hips in that dance number, blowing behind as he cut and wove through heavy traffic—taxis and buses and Cadillacs—uptown, downtown, Broadway, then over to his hotel to see just how hard she'd be. . . Yeah. He'd like to paint that. Rita was all right. All he had to do was make it to New York. Then her mom would have something to tell the people around here.

But no, that's no reason, nothing but vanity. Good times were fine, but he had to use his painting for. . . Maybe he'd write to Cardinal Cook. They'd give him a room in the basement of Saint Patrick's Cathedral like he read those restorers in Florence Italy had. Yeah. Ma would like that. Her name was Florence. If she would've lived she'd've pushed him to do it. She was the only one in the family who understood because she was the only one who felt Jesus. He could see her under all those covers and comforters, shivering and sweating on the davenport Pa fixed up in the parlor so he'd be able to sleep in his bed when he came from the fields. Just two days before the end she stopped her moaning and sat up, sat up when Roy'd been walking by and called him. "Roy, Roy," she cried in her sickness, "Roy, I'm on my way to Jesus. He's gonna take me home, so I have to tell you, Roy, what he wants you to do." God, the way poor Ma was shaking. "Roy, Jesus wants you to use your pictures to spread his name. He wants you, Roy, he wants you to, to put his image on vinyl, vinyl." Then she sank back and those were her last words.

What the hell did Ma mean? Vinyl what? Then, as he stared into the sun dying orange and golden over the fields, it came to him, the sign he'd waited for. As the heavenly light blinded his eyes he saw them, Fords and Chryslers and Pontiacs and Ramblers, Jeeps and cross-country Greyhounds like the one he'd ride to New York, he saw them, clear, at the end of some giant assembly line, cars of every size and color and they all had God's image, bright, smiling from Roy's bumper sticker.

Floating light, transparent, rippled from the center, washed the medieval walls from apse to chancel, divine vestment, as Terence Cardinal Cook, Archbishop, leaning noticeably on his crozier, weak from prayer, followed incense and acolyte, chasubled, from under the altar. Down Fifth Avenue, past department stores and hotels, chasing the siren of the lead police cycle, Roy's limousine speeds up to the cathedral and smoothly stops. Satin-suited arms help Roy out, lead him to the heavy door where the Cardinal embraces him, says a few private words, and ushers him inside. The organ crashes, the choir roars, and there on a red velvet pillow sits the relic, the artist's proof, the decal. The bells. . . Roy shook his head. Dinner already. He could barely see his sister-in-law beating the triangle. He'd still be twenty minutes washing down the dairy. The half light darkened and Roy went to the door, took a deep breath of that good country air and turned on the electric light.

# PABLO NERUDA

THOMAS PARKINSON

They burned your books and papers. You were dead,
All the power in the world backed them. Dead of cancer,
Dead of bullets from the junta, whatever, you were dead.
They burned your books and papers. Thinking, if they
Think, they, they, that this would destroy you even in your death.

O great master of the hemisphere, I see a new constellation,
The sky is full of a new fire, your burning books and papers,
Your body like Orion, your hair streaming in the firmament,
All that love and politics, and I see a thin country,
Like the California I loved, you are Joaquin, gentle vengeful
Spirit, and you are cursing with your love the horrors of
        my country,
As I curse with my love the horrors of Chile. Murder wells
From my floor, floods with blood my daughter's bed, stains
My dog and congests the keys of my mind until my whole
Residence on earth is clogged with scabrous books.

O great master of the hemisphere, your mastery is the sky
Ingesting evil and vicious women and tyrants of heads swollen
With head-lust, intellects sold to lice in eyes crouching
By the general's bedpost, crawling toward his ambitious crotch,
Where he will rip with his claws until blood flows over
His pillow and he never awakes. He will go down on himself

In a tearing frenzy and seek the green that Lorca wanted,
With Franco, with Nixon, with Salazar, and the Greek
And Chilean and American generals will turn to carbon.

Master, master, tormented master of life and poems here
Is one of your papers. They will fly about the world,
They will infest the funnels of bombers, they will blind
And mute mouths and eyes of liars, they will liberate
Legions of damned men and women from Christian bondage.
As long as one soul is damned I am not saved, as long
As there is no justice I am not innocent, as long
As your papers and books are burning, I am burning.
They will burn forever, over strange southern skies
I have never seen, over Mount Tamalpais, over my house,
Over the Andes, over Allende's grave, over yours, burning,
Burning. Master freed by your poems, freed
By the passion of men and women brooding over your books,
Seeking what you accomplished. You create poets indolently
As the fire rises into a storm that consumes and purifies.
There has never been anyone like you. There will be many
Like you. Easy in your release you fix forever and forever
New stars, and the sky stirs in its peace, and rejoices.

# NOTES ON CONTRIBUTORS

WALTER ABISH's novel *Alphabetical Africa* was published earlier this year by New Directions. His next book, a collection of short fictions, will be brought out in the near future.

An entire book of DAVID ANTIN's "talk-poems" is now being transcribed. A poet and critic with a number of previous volumes to his credit, Antin is Professor of Visual Arts at the University of California, San Diego.

The Mexican poet HOMERO ARIDJIS was born in Contepec, Michoacán, in 1940. Founder and editor of the magazine *Correspondencias*, his books include *Los Espacios Azules* and *Ajedrez, Navegaciones*. BRIAN SWANN is the editor and translator, with Ruth Feldman, of *The Collected Poems of Lucio Piccolo* (Princeton, 1973) and the forthcoming *Selected Poems of Andrea Zanzotto*.

A practicing physician, MARTIN BAX is also editor of the British literary periodical *Ambit*. New Directions will soon publish *The Hospital Ship*, from which "The Crucifixion Disease" is taken.

CID CORMAN lives in Kyoto, where he publishes and edits *Origin*. Among his more recent poetry collections are *Be Quest* (Elizabeth Press) and, from New Directions, *Livingdying* and *Sun Rock Man*.

*Island People*, from which "First Person Biography" is excerpted, is COLEMAN DOWELL's third novel. His satirical American fantasy *Mrs. October Was Here* was published last April by New Directions, and *One of the Children Is Crying*, his first book, was brought out by Random House in 1968.

It was the late Pablo Neruda, speaking of "your wide-open American poetry," who inspired the title of LAWRENCE FERLINGHETTI's most recent collection, *Open Eye, Open Heart* (1973). Owner and publisher of City Lights Books, and a leading figure of the San Francisco cultural scene, the prolific Ferlinghetti has to date contributed ten books—poetry, prose, and drama—to the New Directions list.

WARREN JAY HECHT was born in Brooklyn and now lives in Ann Arbor, where he works for Street Fiction Press as editor of *The Periodical Lunch* and *Anon*, and also teaches at the University of Michigan.

The young Japanese writer YUMIKO KURAHASHI has contributed short stories to two previous numbers of the New Directions anthology, *ND24* ("The Ugly Devils") and *ND26* ("Partei"). Her translators, SAMUEL GROLMES and his wife, YUMIKO TSUMURA, are now completing their work on Miss Kurahashi's novel *The Floating Bridge of Dreams*.

DENISE LEVERTOV's poem "In Thai Binh (Peace) Province" was written in the fall of 1972 during a visit to North Vietnam. A full account of her observations, "Glimpses of Vietnamese Life," is included in *The Poet in the World* (New Directions, 1973), Miss Levertov's first prose collection.

Biographical information on ARTUR LUNDKVIST will be found in the note preceding his "Eight Poems." LEIF SJÖBERG, who teaches at the State University of New York at Stony Brook, collaborated with the late W. H. AUDEN on a number of translations, including Dag Hammarskjöld's *Markings* (Knopf, 1964).

MARICHIKO is a young Kyoto woman poet who takes her pen name from Marichi, the Hindu goddess of the dawn. A larger selection of her work in translation can be found in KENNETH REXROTH's latest volume, *New Poems* (New Directions, 1974).

Earlier this year the poet-playwright MICHAEL MCCLURE had two plays produced on the West Coast—*Gorf* (San Francisco) and *The Derby* (Los Angeles)—and New Directions brought out *September Blackberries*, his newest book of poems.

TOBY OLSON has published six books of poetry, and two new collections, *The Wrestlers and Other Poems* (Barlenmir House) and *Changing Appearance* (Membrane Press), will be brought out soon. "Corridors" is a section of his novel *The Life of Jesus*, other portions of which have appeared in *Lillabulero*, *The Mysterious Barricades*, *Center*, and *For Now*. He is currently at work on his second novel.

THOMAS PARKINSON teaches at the University of California at Berkeley. *Protect the Earth,* a volume of his verse, was published in 1970 by City Lights.

An associate professor of English at the State University of New York at Brockport, A. POULIN, JR. is the author of the book of poems *In Advent* (Dutton, 1972). His translation of Rilke's *Duino Elegies* recently appeared in *American Poetry Review.*

JAMES PURDY has been a frequent contributor to this anthology series, beginning with *ND16* (1957). *Children Is All,* his collection of stories and two short plays, was first published by New Directions in 1962 and is available as an ND Paperbook.

PIERO SANAVIO, who was born in Venice, has lived in Puerto Rico and the United States, and now makes his home in Rome. Among his published works, in Italy, are a novel and critical studies of Thoreau, Pound, and modern French poetry.

TENNESSEE WILLIAMS's presence in the modern theatre is by now almost legendary. Yet he is also a master of poetry and fiction. *In the Winter of Cities,* his collected poems, was brought out by New Directions in 1956, and this year his most recent volume of short stories, *Eight Mortal Ladies Possessed,* made its appearance.

AL YOUNG teaches at the Creative Writing Center at Stanford University. His first poetry collection, *Dancing,* was published in 1969 by Corinth Books. This was followed by *Song Turning Back into Itself* (1971) and the novel *Snakes* (1972), both brought out by Holt, Rinehart and Winston. A new novel, *Who Is Angelina?,* appeared earlier this year.